THE
RULES
OF
MATHS

John Connor JP BSc
Headmaster of Hale Preparatory School
and
Patricia Soper

Dedicated to
the past, present and future
pupils of Hale Preparatory School

ORIFLAMME PUBLISHING

0 948093 06 4

First edition 1989
Second edition 1990
Third edition 1991
Fourth edition 1992

Oriflamme Publishing Ltd
60 Charteris Road London N4 3AB

Phototypeset in 12 point Century Schoolbook
by Keytec Typesetting, Bridport, Dorset
and printed in the British Isles by
The Guernsey Press Co. Ltd.

INTRODUCTION TO 'THE RULES OF MATHS'
for Parents, Teachers and Pupils

PARENTS

Many parents are naturally concerned about their children's performance in the key subject of mathematics. They are eager to assist and encourage, but do not always possess the 'tools of the trade' to do so.

This book, **The Rules of Maths**, is designed with such parents very much in mind. The maths which children should encounter in their primary and early secondary education has been analysed and consolidated into 21 carefully structured chapters. Each rule, principle or process is dealt with in a clear, easily understood way, with full explanations, worked examples and practice questions. This presentation will enable both parents and children to tackle unfamiliar or difficult methods and concepts with growing skill and confidence.

TEACHERS

The Rules of Maths provides teachers with a comprehensive guide to the essential processes which form the foundations of mathematical knowledge and ability.

While no text book can replace a good mathematics teacher, the present book is designed to enable pupils to work on their own initiative and at their own pace. It provides scope for the revision and practice of skills and methods, together with succinct and intelligible introductions to new concepts and ideas. Much of the teaching content is provided through examples, coupled with careful explanation, clearly presented.

The book is an excellent source of reference, a convenient handbook, and a valuable reinforcement for examinations at 11+, 13+ and even GCSE.

PUPILS

How many times have you forgotten how to do percentages, divide by a fraction or a decimal, or do long division? Do you remember what prime numbers are, or what a factor is?

If this sort of thing happens to you, you should find this book very helpful. All the methods have been explained very fully, where possible without using complicated language. Where there are special or technical words they have also been explained. In each case, we have assumed that you have forgotten *everything*! – So every stage is set out from the beginning, using examples so that you can see how things work in practice.

You will find **The Rules of Maths** useful in class, when doing your homework, for checking up on things you are not sure about, and when you are revising for examinations and tests.

THE RULES OF MATHS

CONTENTS

CHAPTER ONE

NUMBERS

Our number system is worked in the base of 10 and each number has a place value. This means that its **value** depends on its **position**.

This can be shown by the following columns which are used in arithmetic.

Example: 956

(TH)	(H)	(T)	(U)
Thousands	Hundreds	Tens	Units
	9	5	6

As you move from one column to the next, always beginning with units, each number becomes ten times larger. Therefore:

U = 6 units

T = 5 groups of 10   (50)

H = 9 groups of 100 (900)

So, in these numbers the figures underlined have the following values:

3,764   3 = 3,000   (three thousand)

97,647   9 = 90,000 (ninety thousand)

74,652   6 = 600   (six hundred)

When putting words into figures, the word thousand is shown by using a comma, which will be followed by three digits. So, four thousand seven hundred and ninety six becomes 4,796.

In the same way, the word million is represented by a comma. In this case that comma will be followed by six digits. So, seven million twenty one thousand and sixty seven becomes 7,021,067.

Note: that the comma representing the thousands is still inserted.

Certain numbers form groups because they are similar in some way.

1. Even numbers

An even number is a number which can be exactly divided by 2.
Example: 2 4 26 38 100

2. Odd numbers

All other numbers are odd numbers.

3. Prime numbers

A prime number is a number which can only be divided exactly by **itself** and by **one**.
All prime numbers, except for 2, are odd numbers.
1 is not regarded as a prime number.

5, 7, 13, 29 and 53 are examples of prime numbers.

Number patterns

Numbers can be represented by dots and the patterns formed by these dots give three more groups of numbers:-

4. Square numbers

These are numbers whose dots can be arranged in the shape of a square.

Example:

. . .
. . .   3 (rows) $\times$ 3 (columns) = 9
. . .

Following from this any number multiplied by itself will form a square number.

Example:

$7 \times 7 = 49$ $13 \times 13 = 169$

The square of a number can be written as 7^2. This means 7×7 – seven rows and seven columns. So 7^2 is 49.

With a square number, the number of dots in each row, or in each column, is called the **square root** of the number.

So

. . . . .
. . . . .
. . . . .   There are 25 dots – so the square number is 25.
. . . . .   There are 5 dots in each row (and also, of course, 5 in each column).
. . . . .   So 5 is the square root of 25.

In the same way, 7 is the square root of 49, and 13 is the square root of 169.

There is a special sign for the square root: $\sqrt{}$

$\sqrt{49}$ means **the square root of 49** – which is 7.

5. Rectangular numbers

These are numbers whose dots can be arranged into the shape of a rectangle.

Example: · · · · · ·   2 (rows) × 6 (columns) = 12
　　　　　　 · · · · · ·

6. Triangular numbers

These are numbers whose dots can be arranged in the form of a triangle.

Example: 　·
　　　　　· ·   So 6 is a triangular number.
　　　　· · ·

Note: Some numbers are both square and rectangular. *For example:* 16 = 4 × 4 (a square) or 8 × 2 (a rectangle).

36 is the lowest number which is square, rectangular and triangular:-

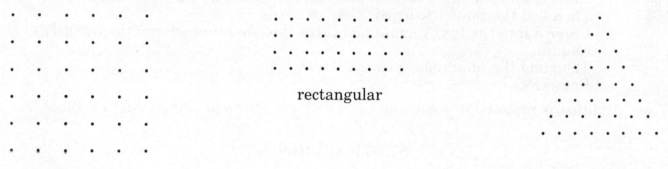

square　　　　　　　　　　rectangular　　　　　　　　　triangular

7

CHAPTER TWO

THE FOUR RULES

The four rules are:- addition (+), subtraction (−), multiplication (×) and division (÷)

ADDITION

Example: 567 + 986

First set the sum out in columns – units under units, tens under tens, etc.

It may be helpful to put "u" over the unit numbers to ensure that all the numbers are in the correct columns.

```
    u    u                        u
567 + 986        becomes:-       567
                                 986 +
```

```
 567      Add the units: 6 + 7 = 13.
 986 +    Enter 3 into the units column and carry the ten into the tens column.
1553      Then add the tens: 1 (carried) + 8 + 6 = 15.
 1 1      Enter 5 into the tens column and carry the one hundred into the hundreds
          column.
          Then add the hundreds: 1 (carried) + 9 + 5 = 15.
          Enter 15.
```

Note: Addition is replaced in some questions by "add", "sum of", "increase", or "plus".

SUBTRACTION

For example: 97 − 15
Set down the sum in columns, as in Addition:

```
t u
9 7      First subtract the units by saying 7 take away 5.
1 5 −    Then subtract the tens by saying 9 take away 1.
8 2
```

Here is another example: 53 − 27

```
t u
5 3      It is not always possible to take away the bottom number from the top
2 7 −    number, because the bottom number is bigger.
2 6
```

```
 t   u
4̶5̶ ¹3   First subtract the units: 3 − 7. This is impossible.
 2   7   Therefore, borrow one from the tens and add the "ten" to the 3.
 2   6   The 3 becomes 13 (10 + 3) and the five is reduced to 4.
         Now say 13 take away 7. This equals 6. Then say 4 take away 2 is 2.
         Then say 4 take away 2 is 2.
```

Sometimes it is impossible to borrow from the next column. In this case the "next" column must borrow first, as in the following example:-

h	t	u	
9	0	4	Four take away 5 is impossible. Therefore borrow from the next column.
1	7	5	This is impossible in this sum. The tens column needs to borrow first.

Thus the top line becomes 8 (10) 4.

The units column can now borrow from the tens column giving a top line 8 9 14

h	t	u
$^8\cancel{9}$ $^9\cancel{10}$		$^1 4$
1	7	5
7	2	9

Note: "Subtraction" is often replaced by "difference", "reduce", "minus".

MULTIPLICATION

Example: 96×5.   Set out the sum as follows:

```
  9 6
×   5
4 8 0
  3
```

Say $6 \times 5 = 30$. Enter the unit and carry the 3 tens.
Then $9 \times 5 = 45$. Add on the 3 carried $= 48$.

In long multiplication, carry out two separate multiplications and add the two answers together:

Example: 934×26

```
    9 3 4
×     2 6
  5 6 0 4
1 8 6 8 0
2 4 2 8 4
1 1
```

First multiply by the 6 by saying 4×6, 3×6 and 9×6 (as in a simple multiplication sum). This is the first line of the answer.

Then multiply by the 2. But the 2 is in fact 20. Therefore put 0 down before you start multiplying, so the answer starts in the tens column. 4×2, 3×2 and 9×2. This is the second line of the answer.

Then add the answers of the two multiplications together.

If you multiply by a three digit number, put down 0 0 before multiplying by the hundreds number.

Example: 974×213

In this example, before multiplying by the 2 (two hundred), two noughts are put down.

```
      974
×     213
     2922
     9740
   194800
   207462
   1 1 2
```

Obviously multiplication (times) becomes impossible unless you know the tables up to 9 perfectly.

DIVISION

Example: 497 ÷ 6.

The sum is set out like this:- $6\overline{)497}$

$$\frac{8\ 2}{6\overline{)49^{1}7}}\ \text{r}\ 5$$

Say 6 into 4. This will not divide so "carry" the 4 to the 9.

Then say 6 into 49. 6 goes into 48, 8 times (6 × 8 = 48) with a remainder of 1. Write the 8 on the top line. The remainder (1) is placed in front of the 7.

Then say 6 into 17. This goes 2 times (2 × 6 = 12) with 5 left over. Write the 2 on the top line.

Since there are no further numbers, the five becomes a remainder. Write in the remainder.

When dividing by a two digit number more than 12, it is usually best to use long division:

Example: 798 ÷ 15.

The sum is set out like this:- $15\overline{)798}$

$$\begin{array}{r} 53\ \text{r}\ 3 \\ 15\overline{)798} \\ -75 \\ \hline 48 \\ -45 \\ \hline 3 \end{array}$$

$$\begin{array}{cc} 15 & 15 \\ \times 4 & \times 5 \\ \hline 60 & 75 \end{array}$$

$$\begin{array}{c} 15 \\ \times 6 \\ \hline 90 \end{array}$$

Say 15 into 7 will not divide. Then "carry" the 7 to the 9.

Then say, how many times will 15 go into 79? Often a number of "trial" multiplication sums is necessary to discover the correct answer. For example 4 × 15 = 60 is too low, 6 × 15 = 90 is too high. These should be tried out at the side of the sum. Always show this working neatly.

15 into 79 goes 5 times (15 × 5 = 75).

Enter the 5 above the "9" and the 75 below the "79". Subtract 75 from 79 to find the remainder (4).

Bring down the 8 to the remainder, making 48. Repeat the procedure. How many times will 15 go into 48? The answer is 3 (15 × 3 = 45). Put the 3 above and the 45 below the 48. Subtract 45 from 48.

As there are no more figures, the 3 left is the remainder.

CHAPTER THREE

FRACTIONS

When a whole amount or a whole number is divided into equal parts, each part is known as a **fraction** of the whole.

Look at the circle and square:-

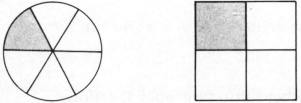

The circle has been divided into six equal parts. One of those parts has been shaded. We call this one sixth, or a sixth. In fractions one sixth is written like this: $\frac{1}{6}$.

The unshaded parts make up five sixths, written $\frac{5}{6}$, of the circle.

The square has been divided into four equal parts, with one of them shaded so $\frac{1}{4}$ is shaded and $\frac{3}{4}$ are unshaded. (We can call this 'one fourth' and 'three fourths', but it is more usual to say 'one quarter' and 'three quarters'.)

There are five important terms which need to be known:

1. The Denominator

The denominator is the bottom line of the fraction.
It tells us how many equal parts the whole is divided into.
So $\frac{1}{4}$ – the whole is divided into 4 equal parts.

2. The Numerator

The numerator is the top line of the fraction.
It tells us how many of the equal parts have been taken.
So $\frac{3}{5}$ – the whole is divided into five equal parts and three are taken.

3. A Proper Fraction (also called a Vulgar Fraction)

A proper fraction is one in which the numerator is smaller than the denominator.

Example: $\frac{2}{17}$, $\frac{19}{26}$

All these fractions are less than a whole one.

4. An Improper Fraction

An improper fraction is one in which the numerator is *larger* than the denominator.

Example: $\frac{15}{8}$, $\frac{17}{5}$

All improper fractions like these are *larger* than one.

5. A Mixed Number

A mixed number is a combination of a whole number and a fraction.

Example: $4\frac{1}{5}$, $8\frac{3}{4}$

Making mixed numbers into improper fractions:

All mixed numbers can be made into improper fractions by using three stages:

Example: $2\frac{3}{4}$ can be written as $\frac{11}{4}$

  (i) Multiply the whole number by the denominator: $4 \times 2 = 8$

 (ii) To this result add the numerator: $8 + 3 = 11$

(iii) Put the final answer over the orginal denominator: $\frac{11}{4}$

Making improper fractions into mixed numbers:

All improper fractions can be made into mixed numbers by using three stages:

Example: $\frac{17}{5}$ can be written as $3\frac{2}{5}$

  (i) Divide the denominator into the numerator: $5\overline{)17}$ r. 2 with quotient 3

 (ii) Put the remainder over the original denominator: $\frac{2}{5}$

(iii) Bring the whole number and the fraction together to give the final answer: $3\frac{2}{5}$

In the case of an improper fraction such as $\frac{18}{3}$, the answer is a whole number: 6.

Finding the value of a fraction:

Example: The value of $\frac{3}{5}$ of 20 is 12.

This is achieved in two stages:

  (i) Divide the whole amount by the denominator: $20 \div 5 = 4$

 (ii) Multiply the answer by the numerator: $4 \times 3 = 12$

Equivalent Fractions

Look at these two squares:

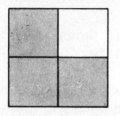

(a) Divided into four
    equal parts

Three shaded – $\dfrac{3}{4}$

(b) Divided into sixteen
    equal parts

Twelve shaded – $\dfrac{12}{16}$

In each diagram the same amount of the shape has been shaded. Therefore we can see that $\frac{3}{4}$ and $\frac{12}{16}$ are fractions which have the same value. They are called **equivalent fractions**.

The fractions $\frac{3}{4}$ and $\frac{12}{16}$ have a connection. If the numerator of $\frac{3}{4}$ is multiplied by four, the answer is twelve and if its denominator is multiplied by four, the answer is sixteen.

In the same way, if both the numerator and denominator of $\frac{3}{5}$ are multiplied by five, the answer is $\frac{15}{25}$. $\frac{15}{25}$ is an equivalent fraction to $\frac{3}{5}$.

This leads to an important rule:-

The denominator and numerator of a fraction can be multiplied by the same number without changing the value of the fraction.

Cancelling

The numerator and denominator of a fraction can also be *divided* **by the same number**, without changing the value of the fraction.

This process is very useful, as it helps to make the numbers involved smaller and easier to deal with, while keeping the fraction's value the same.

The process is known as **cancelling**.

When a fraction cannot be cancelled any further, it is said to be in its **lowest terms**.

$\frac{12}{24}$ can be divided down to $\frac{6}{12}$ (by dividing the numerator and denominator by 2). But, since $\frac{6}{12}$ can be further cancelled, the fraction is not expressed in its lowest terms.

$\frac{12}{24}$ cancelled to $\frac{1}{2}$ (dividing numerator and denominator by 12) is expressed in its lowest terms since no further cancelling is possible.

The Common Denominator

When required to put fractions in order, from smallest to largest, or the other way round, it is necessary to find a denominator which can be used for all the fractions.

This means a number must be found into which all the existing denominators will divide exactly, and such a number is called **the common denominator**.

(i) Always try to find the **lowest common denominator**. This is the **lowest** number into which all the denominators of the fractions you are dealing with will divide.

(ii) For each fraction, find the number its denominator has been multiplied by to get to the common denominator, then multiply the numerator by the same number.

Example: Put into ascending order:-

$$\frac{3}{4} \quad \frac{1}{2} \quad \frac{11}{12} \quad \frac{5}{6} \quad \frac{7}{8}$$

One possible common denominator for all these fractions is 48, but the lowest common denominator is 24.

Note: The lowest common denominator is sometimes called the lowest common multiple.

Work through the fractions:

$\frac{3}{4}$ Multiply the denominator by six to make twenty-four, so make sure the numerator is multiplied by six as well:

$$\frac{3}{4} = \frac{18}{24}$$

$\frac{1}{2}$ Multiply the denominator by 12, so the numerator by 12 as well:

$$\frac{1}{2} = \frac{12}{24}$$

Continue in this way with each fraction.

It is now possible to put the new fractions you have worked out in ascending order, by studying the numerator:

$$\frac{12}{24} \quad \frac{18}{24} \quad \frac{20}{24} \quad \frac{21}{24} \quad \frac{22}{24}$$

Finally, write in the original fractions for which these are the equivalents:

$$\frac{1}{2} \quad \frac{3}{4} \quad \frac{5}{6} \quad \frac{7}{8} \quad \frac{1}{12}$$

TYPICAL QUESTIONS

1. For each of the following shapes, write down in words and figures the fraction that has been shaded.

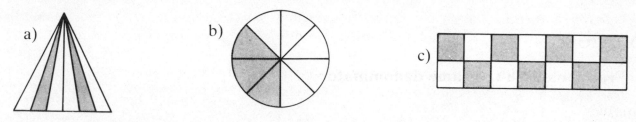

a)   b)   c)

2. Two of the fractions in Question 1 can be cancelled. State which they are and reduce each to its lowest terms.

3. Give the corrrect terms for the following:

    (a) A fraction where the number on the top line is larger than that on the bottom line.
    (b) A fraction where the numerator is smaller than the denominator.
    (c) Two fractions which have the same value.
    (d) The lowest possible number into which all the denominators of a group of fractions will divide exactly.

4. Express these mixed numbers as improper fractions:

    (a) $3\frac{4}{5}$ (b) $18\frac{1}{2}$ (c) $7\frac{10}{11}$ (d) $9\frac{2}{3}$ (e) $6\frac{7}{9}$

5. Express these improper fractions as mixed numbers:

    (a) $\frac{19}{5}$ (b) $\frac{19}{11}$ (c) $\frac{24}{7}$ (d) $\frac{63}{8}$ (e) $\frac{46}{3}$

6. Find:

    (a) $\frac{3}{4}$ of 20   (b) $\frac{5}{8}$ of 56   (c) $\frac{4}{5}$ of 1280   (d) $\frac{2}{3}$ of 1203

7. Put these fractions into their lowest terms:

    (a) $\frac{6}{24}$ (b) $\frac{40}{72}$ (c) $\frac{9}{45}$

8. Put these fractions into ascending order of size:

    (a) $\frac{9}{15}$ $\frac{3}{5}$ $\frac{2}{3}$ $\frac{1}{2}$ $\frac{7}{30}$

THE FOUR RULES OF FRACTIONS

ADDITION

(a) Fractions with the same denominator

Example: $\dfrac{5}{11} + \dfrac{3}{11}$

Since the denominators are the same in both cases, simply add the numerators and put the answer over the **same** denominator i.e. $5 + 3 = 8$. This gives $\frac{8}{11}$

Note: Do not add the two denominators.
If the answer is an improper fraction, e.g. $\frac{7}{2}$, make it into a mixed number.

(b) Fractions with a different denominator

Example: $\dfrac{2}{3} + \dfrac{3}{4}$

Follow these stages:

(i) Find a number into which both denominators will divide. This is the common denominator. In this example, it is 12. *Try always to obtain the lowest common denominator since it will avoid the need to cancel at the end of the sum.*

(ii) Draw a line and put 12 as the denominator: $\dfrac{}{12}$

(iii) Take the first fraction ($\frac{2}{3}$) and divide its denominator into the common denominator: $12 \div 3 = 4$

(iv) Multiply the answer by the numerator of the fraction: $2 \times 4 = 8.$

(v) Place this number on top of the line and put in the plus sign: $\dfrac{8 \quad +}{12}$

(vi) The same procedure is carried out on the second fraction: $12 \div 4 = 3$, $3 \times 3 = 9$. This number is placed on top of the line after the plus sign:

$$\frac{8+9}{12} = \frac{17}{12}$$

This improper fraction is made into a mixed number, so:

$$\frac{2}{3} + \frac{3}{4} = \frac{8+9}{12} = \frac{17}{12} = 1\frac{5}{12}$$

(c) Adding mixed numbers

Example: $4\frac{1}{5} + 3\frac{3}{4}$

Follow these stages:

(i) Add the whole numbers: $\qquad\qquad\qquad\qquad$ $4 + 3 = 7$

(ii) Add the fractions: $\qquad\qquad\qquad\qquad$ $\dfrac{1}{5} + \dfrac{3}{4} = \dfrac{4 + 15}{20} = \dfrac{19}{20}$

Bring the two answers together: $\qquad\qquad$ $7\frac{19}{20}$

Note the following example: $3\frac{3}{4} + 2\frac{5}{6}$

(i) Add the whole numbers: $\qquad\qquad\qquad\qquad$ $3 + 2 = 5$

(ii) Add the fractions $\qquad\qquad\qquad\qquad$ $\dfrac{3}{4} + \dfrac{5}{6} = \dfrac{9 + 10}{12} = \dfrac{19}{12}$

Convert this to a mixed number: $\qquad\qquad$ $1\frac{7}{12}$

(iii) Add the whole number and the mixed number: $\quad 1\frac{7}{12} + 5 = 6\frac{7}{12}$.

SUBTRACTION

Follow the same method as addition, but remember to take away:

Example: $\dfrac{7}{10} - \dfrac{2}{5} = \dfrac{7 - 4}{10} = \dfrac{3}{10}$

Similarly, when subtracting mixed numbers, follow the same method:

Example: $7\frac{1}{3} - 2\frac{1}{5}$

(i) Subtract the whole numbers, $7 - 2 = 5$

(ii) Subtract the fractions, by using the common denominator.

$$\frac{1}{3} - \frac{1}{5} = \frac{5 - 3}{15} = \frac{2}{15}$$

(iii) Bring the two answers together: $5\frac{2}{15}$

The Difficult Case

Example: $7\frac{1}{5} - 2\frac{1}{3}$

(i) $7 - 2 = 5$

(ii) $\dfrac{1}{5} - \dfrac{1}{3} = \dfrac{3 - 5}{15}$

The *difficulty* is that the numerators cannot be subtracted. The following stages are followed:

  (i) Borrow a whole one from the 5. So, 5 becomes 4.

  (ii) Convert the "whole" into the same fraction as the common denominator: $\dfrac{15}{15}$

  (iii) Add the whole on to the first fraction: $\dfrac{(15 + 3) - 5}{15}$

  (iv) Then subtract: $\dfrac{18 - 5}{15} = \dfrac{13}{15}$

  (v) Bring the two answers together: $4\frac{13}{15}$

MULTIPLICATION:

(a) Multiplying two proper fractions
Multiply the top number by the top number and the bottom number by the bottom number.

Example: $\dfrac{1}{3} \times \dfrac{5}{7} = \dfrac{1 \times 5}{3 \times 7} = \dfrac{5}{21}$

Before multiplying, check to see if it is possible to cancel down **any** numerator with **any** denominator.

Example: $\dfrac{2}{15} \times \dfrac{9}{10}$ becomes $\dfrac{1}{5} \times \dfrac{3}{5}$

because 2 and 10 have both been divided by 2;
and 9 and 15 have both been divided by 3.

(b) Multiplying mixed numbers

Example: $2\frac{1}{4} \times 2\frac{2}{3}$

Follow these stages:

  (i) Make the mixed numbers into improper fractions

  $\dfrac{9}{4} \times \dfrac{8}{3}$

  (ii) Cancel down **any** numerator with **any** denominator if they can both be divided by the same number.

  $\dfrac{{}^{3}\cancel{9}}{{}_{1}\cancel{4}} \times \dfrac{{}^{2}\cancel{8}}{{}_{1}\cancel{3}} = \dfrac{3}{1} \times \dfrac{2}{1}$

(iii) Multiply the top by the top and the bottom by the bottom.

$$\frac{3}{1} \times \frac{2}{1} = \frac{6}{1} = 6$$

When multiplying a whole number by a fraction, it is usually better to put the whole number over 1.

Example: $3 \times 3\frac{1}{2}$ becomes $\frac{3}{1} \times \frac{7}{2}$

In fractions "of" always means multiply.

DIVISION

(a) **Dividing two proper fractions**

Example: $\frac{6}{7} \div \frac{3}{7}$

When dividing three stages are followed:

(i) Turn the **divisor** upside down. The divisor is the number you are dividing by: that is, the **second number**.

So $\frac{3}{7}$ becomes $\frac{7}{3}$

(ii) Change the division sign to a multiplication sign:

$$\frac{6}{7} \times \frac{7}{3}$$

(iii) Multiply the fractions out as usual:

$$\frac{{}^2\cancel{6}}{{}_1\cancel{7}} \times \frac{{}^1\cancel{7}}{{}_1\cancel{3}} = \frac{2}{1} \times \frac{1}{1} = \frac{2}{1} = 2$$

(b) **Dividing mixed numbers:**

Example: $1\frac{7}{8} \div 4\frac{1}{2}$

Four stages are followed:

(i) Make the mixed numbers into improper fractions:

$$\frac{15}{8} \div \frac{9}{2}$$

(ii) Turn the divisor upside down:

$$\frac{9}{2} \text{ becomes } \frac{2}{9}$$

19

(iii) Change the division sign into a multiplication sign:

$$\frac{15}{8} \times \frac{2}{9}$$

(iv) Cancel down and multiply:

$$\frac{\overset{5}{\cancel{15}}}{\underset{4}{\cancel{8}}} \times \frac{\overset{1}{\cancel{2}}}{\underset{3}{\cancel{9}}} = \frac{5}{4} \times \frac{1}{3} = \frac{5}{12}$$

TYPICAL QUESTIONS

1. (a) $\frac{6}{7} + \frac{9}{7}$ (b) $\frac{7}{11} + \frac{2}{11}$ (c) $\frac{2}{5} + \frac{3}{5}$

2. (a) $\frac{2}{5} + \frac{3}{10}$ (b) $\frac{1}{4} + \frac{1}{3}$ (c) $\frac{5}{8} + \frac{3}{4}$ (d) $\frac{3}{7} + \frac{1}{2}$

Ensure you find the lowest common denominator in this and the next three questions.

3. (a) $4\frac{2}{3} + 1\frac{1}{4}$ (b) $2\frac{1}{5} + 3\frac{3}{4}$ (c) $1\frac{5}{7} + 2\frac{2}{3}$ (d) $2\frac{7}{8} + \frac{4}{5}$

4. (a) $\frac{3}{4} - \frac{5}{8}$ (b) $\frac{4}{9} - \frac{1}{6}$ (c) $7\frac{5}{6} - 5\frac{1}{2}$ (d) $9\frac{2}{3} - 4\frac{1}{4}$

5. (a) $9\frac{3}{5} - 6\frac{7}{10}$ (b) $2\frac{1}{2} - \frac{3}{4}$ (c) $7\frac{1}{6} - 6\frac{3}{8}$ (d) $8\frac{2}{7} - 3\frac{3}{4}$

6. (a) $\frac{1}{4} \times \frac{3}{8}$ (b) $\frac{7}{9} \times \frac{4}{11}$ (c) $\frac{2}{3} \times \frac{5}{6}$ (d) $\frac{3}{5} \times \frac{5}{9}$

7. (a) $\frac{1}{6} \div \frac{2}{7}$ (b) $\frac{3}{4} \div \frac{3}{5}$ (c) $\frac{15}{17} \div \frac{5}{34}$ (d) $\frac{1}{8} \div \frac{3}{4}$

8. (a) $2\frac{2}{5} \times 3\frac{1}{4}$ (b) $4\frac{2}{3} \div 5\frac{4}{9}$ (c) $4\frac{1}{8} \times 7\frac{3}{11}$ (d) $6\frac{6}{7} \div 2\frac{10}{21}$

9. What are (a) three quarters of two ninths, and (b) $\frac{5}{7}$ of $8\frac{2}{5}$?

10. How much would each child get if you shared $3\frac{1}{2}$ oranges among four children?

20

CHAPTER FOUR
PERCENTAGES

Percentages are simply fractions expressed in a different way.

Percent or **percentage** means **part of a hundred**.

The sign % means percentage or percent.

We use percentages when we work out examination results, statistics (for example it might be discovered that 85% of all children can't do percentages), price reductions (special offers – 10% off), and profits.

Converting fractions into percentages

All fractions can be converted into percentages.

To make a fraction into a percentage, multiply the fraction by 100.

Example: Express $\frac{3}{5}$ as a percentage.

There are four key facts:

(i) $\frac{3}{5}$ means three-fifths of a whole.

(ii) In percentages, a whole is 100%

(iii) Therefore, it is necessary to find $\frac{3}{5}$ of 100.

(iv) In fractions "of" means multiply.

When the sum is written out, the whole number (100) should be written as $\frac{100}{1}$

So $\frac{3}{5}$ of 100 becomes $\frac{3}{5} \times \frac{100}{1}$

$$\frac{3}{{}_1\cancel{5}} \times \frac{\overset{20}{\cancel{100}}}{1} = \frac{60}{1} = 60$$

Put in the percentage sign.
The answer is 60%

Converting percentages into fractions

All percentages can be converted into fractions.

Write the percentage as a fraction with 100 as its denominator, then cancel it down if possible.

Example: Express 75% as a fraction.

There are three stages:

(i) Take away the percentage sign.

(ii) Write the seventy-five as part of a hundred: $\dfrac{75}{100}$

(iii) Cancel down the fraction: $\dfrac{75}{100} = \dfrac{3}{4}$

Answer: $75\% = \frac{3}{4}$

Converting difficult percentages into fractions

"Difficult" percentages are those percentages which **already have a fraction in them.**

Example: $87\frac{1}{2}\%$

To make this percentage into a fraction, there are four stages:

(i) Take away the percentage sign and write as a fraction over 100: $\dfrac{87\frac{1}{2}}{100}$

(ii) Multiply $87\frac{1}{2}$ by 2 (*because 2 is the denominator of the fraction*)

$87\frac{1}{2} \times 2 = 175$

(iii) Then multiply the 100 on the bottom line by $2 = 200$

(iv) The fraction is now $\dfrac{175}{200}$.

Then cancel: $\dfrac{175}{200} = \dfrac{35}{40} = \dfrac{7}{8}$

So $87\frac{1}{2}\% = \frac{7}{8}$

Example:

Express $33\frac{1}{3}\%$ as a fraction

  (i) Write as a fraction over 100: $\dfrac{33\frac{1}{3}}{100}$

 (ii) Multiply by 3 (*because 3 is the denominator of the fraction*): $33\frac{1}{3} \times 3 = 100$

(iii) Multiply the 100 on the bottom line by $3 = 300$

 (iv) The new fraction $= \dfrac{100}{300}$

        Cancel down: $\dfrac{100}{300} = \dfrac{1}{3}$

                  $33\frac{1}{3}\% = \frac{1}{3}$

Finding a percentage of an amount

Express the percentage as a fraction. Then, using rules of fractions, find the amount.

Example: Find 45% of £120

Write the percentage as a fraction: $\dfrac{45}{100}$

Then cancel: $\dfrac{45}{100} = \dfrac{9}{20}$

Then carry out the multiplication:

$$\dfrac{9}{\cancel{20}_{1}} \times \dfrac{{}^{6}\cancel{120}}{1} = \dfrac{54}{1} = 54.$$

45% of £120 = £54.

Some percentage values which are useful to remember:

$\frac{1}{2} = 50\%, \ \frac{1}{4} = 25\%, \ \frac{1}{5} = 20\%, \ \frac{1}{10} = 10\%, \ \frac{1}{3} = 33\frac{1}{3}\%$

TYPICAL QUESTIONS

1. Express the following fractions as percentages:

  (a) $\dfrac{3}{10}$ (b) $\dfrac{13}{20}$ (c) $\dfrac{3}{8}$

2. Express the following percentages as fractions in their lowest terms:
  (a) 60%   (b) 35%   (c) 24%   (d) $62\frac{1}{2}\%$

3. Calculate the following amounts:

    (a) 60% of 320   (b) 44% of 75   (c) $37\frac{1}{2}$% of 72

4. In a group of forty people, fifteen had fair hair. What percentage of the group did they make up?

    (*First express the 15 as a fraction of the whole.*)

5. In a sale, an article priced £60 is offered at 30% off. What is its sale price?

    This is the method to follow:-

    (i) Express 30% as a fraction:

$$\frac{30}{100} = \frac{3}{10}$$

    (ii) Find $\frac{3}{10}$ of £60: $\frac{\overset{1}{3}}{\underset{1}{\cancel{10}}} \times \frac{\overset{6}{\cancel{60}}}{1} = 18$

    (iii) £60 − £18 = £42, which is the sale price.

6. A shopkeeper buys a chair for £120.00 and sells it at a 20% profit. What is the price he sells it for?

7. A shopkeeper sells a chair for £81, which is a reduction of 10%. What was the original price?

    This is the method to follow:-

    (a) Express 10% as a fraction: $\frac{1}{10}$. This equals the reduction.

    (b) The chair is sold for $\frac{9}{10}$ of the original price, therefore

    (c) $\frac{9}{10}$ = £81

    (d) $\frac{1}{10}$ = £9

    (e) $\frac{10}{10}$ = £90. This is the original price.

8. 20% of the pupils in a school were off with measles, leaving 160 children present. How many pupils were in school?

CHAPTER FIVE

DECIMALS

Decimals form part of our number system based on ten. They are a way of expressing the parts of a whole – in other words another way of writing fractions.

Decimals are indicated by a decimal point. The value of each decimal number after the decimal point depends on that number's place or position. Just as whole numbers are in units, tens, hundreds and so on, decimals are in tenths, hundredths, thousandths, etc.

Look at this number: 746.395

Hundreds	Tens	Units	.	tenths	hundredths	thousandths
7	4	6	.	3	9	5

In this number there are:-

7 hundreds   (700)

4 tens   (40)

6 units   (6)

3 tenths $(\frac{3}{10})$

9 hundredths $(\frac{9}{100})$

5 thousandths $(\frac{5}{1000})$

We read the number as: *seven hundred and forty six **point** three nine five*

Note: The number seven can be written as 7 or 7.0 or 7.00 and the number ninety one as 91, or 91.0 or 91.00 or 91.0000000 for that matter.

Converting Decimals to Fractions

It is very easy to turn a decimal into a fraction.

If there is **one** figure after the decimal point, put the fraction over **ten**.

So, 0.7 is the same as $\frac{7}{10}$; $1.3 = 1\frac{3}{10}$.

If there are **two** figures after the decimal point, put the fraction over **one hundred**.

So 0.37 is the same as $\frac{37}{100}$; $2.09 = 2\frac{9}{100}$.

If there are **three** figures after the decimal point, put the fraction over **one thousand**.

So 0.137 is the same as $\frac{37}{1000}$; $26.009 = 26\frac{9}{1000}$

Converting Fractions to Decimals

All fractions can be converted into decimals.

Example: Convert $\frac{3}{5}$ into a decimal.

Four stages need to be followed.

  (i) Divide the denominator into the numerator:

    $5\overline{)3}$

 (ii) Since the denominator is larger than the numerator, it will not divide, so write a nought in the answer space. After the nought, put a decimal point and also put a decimal point after the dividend. (The "dividend" is the number being divided into.)

    $\frac{0.}{5\overline{)3.}}$

(iii) Put a nought after the decimal point in the dividend and divide.

    $\frac{0.}{5\overline{)3.0}}$ *Five into three goes nought, carry the three across the decimal point to make thirty.*

 (vi) Complete the division and write the answer in the correct place after the decimal point:

    $\frac{0.\ 6}{5\overline{)3.^30}}$ *Five into thirty goes six*

    Therefore: $\frac{3}{5} = 0.6$

Example: Convert $\frac{1}{4}$ into a decimal.

 (i) $4\overline{)1}$ Write down the division sum

(ii) $\frac{0.}{4\overline{)1.}}$ It will not divide, so put in the 0 and the decimal points.

(iii) $\dfrac{0.}{4)\overline{1.{}^10}}$ Put the nought in the dividend and carry the 1.

(iv) $\dfrac{0.\ 2}{4)\overline{1.{}^10}}$ Now divide: four into ten goes two

In this case there is a remainder

Keep dividing until it divides exactly.

If there is a remainder, insert another nought in the dividend and carry the remainder over to this. Then divide again.

(v) $\dfrac{0.\ 2\ 5}{4)\overline{1.{}^10{}^20}}$ *Four into ten goes two – remainder two. Put down another nought and carry the remainder two. Four into twenty goes five.*

Therefore: $\dfrac{1}{4} = 0.25$

TYPICAL QUESTIONS

1. Put the following numbers into descending order:

   0.36   306.06   3.06   0.036   3.0036

2. Put the following into ascending order:

   4.95   4.09   4.095   0.0490   0.0495

3. Convert the following decimals into fractions:
   (a) 0.87   (b) 3.1   (c) 6.080   (d) 0.009

4. Convert the following fractions into decimals:
   (a) $\frac{1}{2}$ (b) $\frac{9}{10}$ (c) $\frac{3}{4}$ (d) $\frac{7}{8}$

5. Arrange the following in numerical order, starting with the smallest:
   0.5 $\frac{3}{4}$ 0.25   0.9 $\frac{2}{5}$ 0.375

*Hint: All the numbers need to be in the **same** form, so that they can be compared. That means that the fractions need to be converted into decimals.*

27

THE FOUR RULES OF DECIMALS

ADDITION

The rule is a very simple one. When adding decimals, make sure that in setting out the sum, all the decimal points are directly below each other. This way, all the figures will be in the right columns. Then simply add as for any other sum.

Example: 3.471 + 9.036 + 17.681

 (i) Write down the decimal framework

 (ii) Put the figures into the framework and add as usual

$$
\begin{array}{r}
3.471 \\
9.036 \\
+17{\cdot}681 \\
\hline
30{\cdot}188 \\
\end{array}
$$
2 1 1

SUBTRACTION

The rule is the same as for addition. First line up the decimal points of the two numbers in the sum. Then fill in the numbers and subtract in the normal way.

Example: 637.361 − 415.42

 (i) Write down the decimal framework

 (ii) Put the figures into the framework and subtract as usual
Note that you can also borrow numbers across the decimal point as in an ordinary sum.

$$
\begin{array}{r}
6\ 3^6\ 7.^13\ 6\ 1 \\
-4\ 1\ 5.\ 4\ 2\ 0 \\
\hline
2\ 2\ 1.\ 9\ 4\ 1 \\
\end{array}
$$

In this sum 415.42 has been written 415.420 to make sure that all the numbers remain in the correct columns when carrying out the subtraction.

MULTIPLICATION

Multiplying by 10, 100 and 1,000

 (i) To multiply by 10, move the decimal point **one** place to the **right**.

   $3.76 \times 10 = 37.6$

   $49.8 \times 10 = 498.0$ (*or simply* 498)

(ii) To multiply by 100 move the decimal point **two** places to the **right**.

$3.765 \times 100 = 376.5$

$49.82 \times 100 = 4982.0$ (*or simply* 4,982)

$0.3 \ \times 100 = \ 30.0$

In the last example, in order to move the decimal point two places to the right, a nought has been inserted after the 0.3.

(iii) To multiply by 1,000 move the decimal point **three** places to the **right**.

$49.824 \times 1000 = 49824.0$ (*or simply* 49,824)

$9.0 \times 1000 = 9,000$

To multiply decimal numbers

Example: 4.62×2.1

This is carried out in three stages:

(i) Ignore the decimal points and set out the sum as for long multiplication. Multiply as usual:

```
   462
  × 21
   462
  9240
  9702
```

(ii) Count the number of figures that come **after** the decimal points in **both** of the numbers you are multiplying:

4.62 has two decimal figures.
2.1 has one decimal figure.

There is a total of three figures.

(iii) The answer to the multiplication must have this **same** number of figures after the decimal point. In this example, three figures. Count from the **right** of your answer and put in the point.
So, $9702 = 9.702$.

DIVISION

Dividing by 10, 100 and 1,000

(i) To divide by 10, move the decimal point **one** place to the **left**.

$49.8 \div 10 = 4.98$

$0.9 \div 10 = 0.09$

In the last example a nought has been inserted in order to be able to move the number into its correct column.

(ii) To divide by 100, move the decimal point **two** places to the **left**.

$376.2 \div 100 = 3.762$

$0.64 \div 100 = 0.0064$

In the last example it was necessary to insert two noughts in order to move the decimal point two places to the left.

(iii) To divide by 1,000 move the decimal point **three** places to the **left**.

$3762.5 \div 1000 = 3.7625$

$9.0 \div 1000 = 0.009$

To divide into a decimal number

Example: $51.03 \div 3$

This is carried out in three stages:

(i) Set out the sum as a usual division sum

$$3 \overline{)51.03}$$

(ii) Put in the decimal point above the decimal point in the dividend

$$3 \overline{)51.03}$$

(iii) Divide as usual

$$\begin{array}{r} 1\ 7.01 \\ 3 \overline{)5^2 1.03} \end{array}$$

In the following example the remainder is carried over the decimal point: $38.55 \div 5$.

$$\begin{array}{r} 7.\ 71 \\ 5 \overline{)38.^3 55} \end{array}$$

To divide two decimal numbers

Example: $2.7 \div 0.02$

This is set out: $0.02 \overline{)2.7}$

You cannot immediately divide by a decimal number. The division is carried out in three stages:

(i) Make the divisor into a whole number by moving the decimal point to the right:

0.02 becomes 2 The decimal point has been moved two places. That is, the divisor has been multiplied by 100.

(ii) Move the decimal point in the dividend the **same** number of places to the right. It may be necessary to add noughts.

2.7 becomes 2.70 → 270

(iii) Set out the sum as a normal division sum and divide as usual:

$$\begin{array}{r} 1\ 3\ 5 \\ 2\overline{)2\ 7^10} \end{array}$$

So, $2.7 \div 0.02 = 135$

In the following example there is a decimal point in the answer. This point will be directly above the decimal point in the dividend.

$15.102 \div 0.03$

This is set out: $0.03\overline{)15.102}$

This becomes:
$$\begin{array}{r} 5\ 0\ 3.\ 4 \\ 3\overline{)1\ 5\ 1^10.^12} \end{array}$$

TYPICAL QUESTIONS

1. Do the following additions of decimals:
   (a) $3.74 + 38.09$ (b) $17.68 + 4.324$ (c) $9.93 + 0.07$

2. Subtract the following:
   (a) $14.9 - 5.2$ (b) $11.01 - 10.1$ (c) $3.7 - 1.096$

3. Multiply the following:
   (a) 3.96×10 (b) 4.823×1000 (c) 0.016×100

4. Multiply these sums:
   (a) 93.75×3.5 (b) 0.1×8.3 (c) 0.08×17.60

5. Divide the following:
   (a) $14.65 \div 10$ (b) $132.9 \div 1000$ (c) $1.4 \div 100$

6. Divide the following:
   (a) $14.104 \div 8$ (b) $18.6 \div 12$ (c) $30.5 \div 20$

7. Carry out these divisions of decimals:
   (a) $3.57 \div 1.7$ (b) $7.02 \div 0.6$ (c) $0.360 \div 0.15$

CHAPTER SIX
MONEY

100 pence = £1

This means all money calculations are carried out using the rules of decimals.

One pound and three pence is written:	£1.03
One pound and thirty pence is written:	£1.30
Two hundred and four pence is written:	£2.04
Two hundred and forty pence is written:	£2.40

It is advised when carrying out calculations in money to:

(i) Always work in pounds. So 37p = £0.37

(ii) Ignore the £ sign until you have a final answer.

Addition

Example: £3.17 + £19.03 + £3.49

This becomes
```
 3.17
19.03
 3.49
25.69        Answer = £25.69
```

Subtraction

Example: £3.09 − £1.97

This becomes
```
²3̸.¹09
1. 97
1. 12        Answer = £1.12
```

Multiplication

Example: £32.56 × 9

This becomes
```
32.56
    9
293.04       Answer = £293.04
```

Division

Example: £46.32 ÷ 3

This becomes
```
  15.44
3)46.32      Answer = £15.44
```

CHAPTER SEVEN

LENGTH, WEIGHT AND CAPACITY

These are all measured in what are called metric units. That means they are measured in groups of 10, 100 or 1000. The four rules are therefore most easily carried out in decimals. So, before carrying out the four rules of addition, subtraction, division and multiplication, the rules of decimals must be learnt thoroughly.

LENGTH

Millimetres are used for small measurements, for example, the thickness of paper.
Centimetres and **metres** are used to measure things like material, or rooms.
Kilometres are used for longer distances such as train journeys.

10 millimetres = 1 centimetre

Each of these dashes is one millimetre (1 mm) long. ----------

This line ⊢⎯⎯⊣ is one centimetre (1 cm) long – as long as 10 of the mm dashes joined together.

To convert millimetres into centimetres divide by 10.

So, 46 mm = 4 centimetres 6 millimetres.
This is written as 4.6 cm.
763 mm = 76 cm 3 mm., written 76.3 cm.

Note: There is always **one** figure after the decimal point because we have divided by 10.

100 centimetres = 1 metre

A long stride is about a metre.

To convert centimetres into metres divide by 100.

So, 350 cm = 3 m 50 cm.
This is written 3.50 m.

905 cm = 9 m 5 cm, written 9.05 m.

Note There are always **two** figures after the decimal point because we have divided by 100.

1000 metres = 1 kilometre

To convert metres into kilometres divide by 1000.

So, 7545 m = 7 km 545 m.
This is written 7.545 km.
5006 m = 5 km 6 m, written 5.006 km.

Note: There are always **three** figures after the decimal point because we have divided by 1000.

To convert   (i) centimetres to millimetres, multiply by 10
                      (ii) metres to centimetres, multiply by 100
                      (iii) kilometres to metres, multiply by 1000

Addition

Example: 3 km 54 metres + 18 km 542 m

This becomes 3.054 km + 18.542 km.
Notice the"0" in 3.054.

Then addition takes place as in the rules of decimals.

$$
\begin{array}{r}
3.054 \\
\underline{18 \cdot 542} \\
21.596 \text{ km}
\end{array}
$$

Subtraction

Example: 3 metres 17 cm − 2 metres 3 cm.

This becomes 3.17 m − 2.03 m

Then subtract as in decimals:

$$
\begin{array}{r}
3.17 \\
\underline{2 \cdot 03} \\
1.14 \text{ m}
\end{array}
$$

Multiplication

Example: 16 km 54 m × 6

This becomes 16.054 km × 6

Then multiply as in decimals:

$$
\begin{array}{r}
16.054 \\
\underline{6} \\
96.324 \text{ km}
\end{array}
$$

Division

Example: 27 m 5 cm ÷ 5

This becomes 27.05 m ÷ 5

Then divide as in decimals:

$$
\begin{array}{r}
\underline{5.41}\text{m} \\
5)\overline{27.05}
\end{array}
$$

EQUIVALENT LENGTHS

Kilometres, metres, centimetres and millimetres have replaced or are replacing miles, yards, feet and inches.

Miles Distances are still measured in miles.
   The distance between Manchester and London is said to be 189 miles.
   5 miles = 8 kilometres approximately,
   so 1 kilometre = $\frac{5}{8}$ mile.

Yards A yard is slightly shorter than a metre.
   1760 yards equals a mile.

Feet 3 feet equal 1 yard.
   1 yard is a little less than 1 metre (100 cm)
   1 foot is approximately 30 cm.

Inches Each foot is divided into 12 parts called inches.
   Each inch is approximately $2\frac{1}{2}$ cm.

WEIGHT

The basic unit, the gram, is used only when buying items that do not weigh much, like sweets, cotton wool, etc.

1000 grams = 1 kilogram

So, 7564 g = 7 kg 564 g. This is written 7.564 kg.
   9076 g = 9 kg 76 g. This is written 9.076 kg.

Note: There are always **three** figures after the decimal point because we have divided by 1000.

Addition

Example: 7 kg 56 g + 19 kg 246 g

becomes 7.056 kg + 19.246 kg

$$\begin{aligned} 7.056 \\ \underline{19{\cdot}246} \\ 26.302 \text{ kg} \end{aligned}$$

Note: the 0 in 7.056 kg.

Subtraction

Example: 13 kg 17 g − 2 kg 450 g

becomes 13.017 kg − 2.450 kg.

$$\begin{array}{r} 13.017 \\ \underline{2 \cdot 450} \\ 10.567 \text{ kg} \end{array}$$

Multiplication

Example: 9 kg 87 g × 7

becomes 9.087 kg × 7

$$\begin{array}{r} 9.087 \\ \underline{7} \\ 63.609 \text{ kg.} \end{array}$$

Division

Example: 17 kg 55 g ÷ 5

becomes 17.055 ÷ 5

$$\begin{array}{r} 3.411 \text{ kg.} \\ \overline{5)17.055} \end{array}$$

CAPACITY

Litres are used to measure liquids such as milk, petrol and lemonade. A litre is a little under two pints.

Millilitres are used for small quantities, e.g. a dose of medicine.
1000 millilitres = 1 litre
To convert millilitres into litres, divide by 1000.

So, 7463 ml = 7 litres 463 ml
This is written 7.463 ℓ

9056 ml = 9 litres 56 ml or 9.056 ℓ

Note: There are always **three** figures after the decimal point because we have divided by 1000.

When carrying out the four rules follow the same method as for grams and kilograms.

So: 3 litres 46 ml + 2 litres 564 ml becomes 3.046 ℓ + 2.564 ℓ

8 litres 76 ml − 5 litres 497 ml becomes 8.076 ℓ − 5.497 ℓ

17 litres 546 ml × 9 becomes 17.546 ℓ × 9

15 litres 55 ml ÷ 5 becomes 15.055 ℓ ÷ 5.

CHAPTER EIGHT

TIME

HOURS MINUTES AND SECONDS

THE FOUR RULES

60 seconds = 1 minute
60 minutes = 1 hour

Therefore, when working in hours/minutes/seconds, remember to work in groups of 60.

Addition

Example: 3 hrs 50 mins + 2 hrs 40 mins
(i) Set out the sum:

Hours	Minutes
3	50
+ 2	40

(ii) Add the minutes. If the answer is more than 60, put the number below the line.

3	50
2	40
	90

(iii) Convert the minutes into hours and minutes, by dividing by 60.

90 mins = 1 hour 30 mins.

(iv) Put the minutes into the minute column and carry the hours into the hour column.
Add the hours.

3	50
2	40
6	30
1	

Subtraction

Example: 5 hrs 20 mins − 2 hrs 40 mins

(i) Set out the sum

Hours	Minutes
5	20
− 2	40

(ii) Subtract the minute column. If this is impossible, borrow an hour. This hour must be converted into minutes and then added to the minutes already in the column. Then subtract.

⁴5̸	⁸⁰2̸0̸
2	40
	40

Notice The 80 minutes is made up of the original 20 minutes plus the 60 minutes borrowed.

(iii) Subtract the hours column.

4		80
2		40
2		40

Multiplication

Example: 3 hrs 40 mins × 7
Follow these stages

(i) Set out the sum

Hours	Minutes
3	40
	× 7

(ii) Multiply the minutes column. If the answer is more than 60, put the number below the line.

3	40
	×7
	280

(iii) Convert the minutes into hours and minutes by dividing by 60.

280 minutes = 4 hours 40 mins.

(iv) Put the minutes into the minute column and carry over the hours.

3	40
	× 7
	40
4	

(v) Multiply the hours and add the hours carried

3	40
	7
25	40
4	

Division

Example: 18 hrs 25 mins ÷ 5
Follow these stages:
(i) Set out the sum:

Hours	Minutes
5) 18	25

(ii) Divide into the hours

Hours	Minutes
3	
5) 18	25
15	
3	

(iii) Convert the hours remaining into minutes $3 \times 60 = 180$ minutes

(iv) Add the answer of stage 2 on to the minutes already in the minutes column.

```
        3
5) 18        25
   15       180
    3       205
```

(iv) Divide into the minutes column

```
      Hours      Minutes
        3          41
5) 18             25
   15            180
    3         5) 205
                  41
```

EQUIVALENT TIMES

12 hour clock	*24 hour clock*
12 midnight	00.00
1 a.m.	01.00
2 a.m. (2.05 a.m.)	02.00 (02.05)
3 a.m.	03.00
4 a.m.	04.00
5 a.m.	05.00
6 a.m.	06.00
7 a.m.	07.00
8 a.m.	08.00
9 a.m.	09.00
10 a.m.	10.00
11 a.m. (11.20 a.m.)	11.00 (11.20)
12 noon	12.00
1 p.m. (1.30 p.m.)	13.00 (13.30)
2 p.m.	14.00
3 p.m. (3.45 p.m.)	15.00 (15.45)
4 p.m.	16.00
5 p.m.	17.00
6 p.m.	18.00
7 p.m.	19.00
8 p.m.	20.00
9 p.m.	21.00
10 p.m.	22.00
11 p.m.	23.00

In the 24 hour clock the point is now often missed out:
23.30 becomes 2330.

TYPICAL PROBLEMS

1. A bus driver makes 5 journeys in 8 hrs 15 mins. What is the average time of each journey?

Method:-

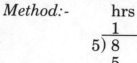

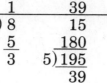

```
            hrs      mins
             1        39
        5) 8          15
           5          180
           3      5) 195
                      39
```

2. A train leaves Manchester at 10.45 a.m. and arrives in Glasgow at 2.42 p.m. How long does the journey take?

It is usual to convert the times of departure and arrival into 24 hour clock times, when a.m. and p.m. time are in the problem. (See table).

```
         hrs       mins
      13 14     102 42
    -    10         45
          3         57
```

CHAPTER NINE

TIME, DISTANCE AND SPEED

The following points should be noted when dealing with problems about time, distance and speed.

TIME

It is usually best to work in hours. Minutes should be expressed as a fraction of an hour. Figures given in minutes must be converted. As there are sixty minutes in one hour:-

10 minutes $= \frac{10}{60} = \frac{1}{6}$ hour.

7 hours 25 minutes $= 7\frac{25}{60} = 7\frac{5}{12}$ hours

DISTANCE

It is usual to work in kilometres. Metres should be expressed as a fraction of a kilometre.

Figures given in metres must be converted, and as there are 1,000 metres in a kilometre:-

3 km 800 m $= 3\frac{800}{1000} = 3\frac{4}{5}$ km.

SPEED

Average speeds are normally given in kilometres per hour (km/hour).
So for example 46 km/hour means that 46 km are covered in one hour.

RULES FOR PROBLEMS

The following facts must be memorized:-
(1) **Distance** = Time of journey × Average speed of journey (**Time × Speed**).
(2) **Speed** = Total distance travelled ÷ Total time taken (**Distance ÷ Time**).
(3) **Time** = Total distance travelled ÷ Average speed of (**Distance ÷ Speed**).
journey

Work carefully through the following examples of the application of these rules:-

(1) Distance

Emma completed a journey in 2 hours 20 minutes, at an average speed of 60 km/h. How far did she travel?

Distance = Time × Speed   = 2 h 20 mins. × 60 = $2\frac{20}{60} \times 60 = 2\frac{1}{3} \times 60$

Multiply according to the rules of fractions:- $\dfrac{7}{\cancel{3}_1} \times \dfrac{\overset{20}{\cancel{60}}}{1} = 140$ km

(2) Speed

Kate completed a journey of 140 km in 2 hours 20 minutes. What was the average speed at which she travelled?

Speed = Distance ÷ Time = 140 ÷ 2 hrs 20 mins.

$$= 140 \div 2\frac{20}{60} = 140 \div 2\frac{1}{3}$$

Divide according to the rules of fractions:-

$$\frac{140}{1} \div \frac{7}{3} = \frac{\overset{20}{\cancel{140}}}{1} \times \frac{3}{\cancel{7}_1} = 60 \text{ km/h}$$

(3) Time

Alison completed a journey of 140 kilometres at an average speed of 60 km/h. How long did the journey take?

Time = Distance ÷ Speed = 140 ÷ 60

The simplest way to perform this division sum is to write it as a fraction:- $\dfrac{140}{60}$

Then cancel: $\dfrac{140}{60} = \dfrac{7}{3} = 2\frac{1}{3}$ hours

The fraction of the hour should then be converted back into minutes:-

$2\frac{1}{3}$ hours = 2 hours 20 minutes.

Rather more complicated problems may involve some extra stages in the process, as in the following examples:-

42

(1) Express a speed of 800 metres covered in 1 minute 20 seconds as a speed in km/h. The steps which need to be taken are as follows:-

1 min 20 secs	= 800 metres
80 secs	= 800 metres
1 second	= 10 metres (800 ÷ 80)
1 minute (60 secs.)	= 600 metres (10 × 60)
1 hour (60 mins.)	= 36,000 metres (600 × 60)
	36,000 metres = 36 kilometres.

Therefore the speed is 36 km/h.

(2) If 50 metres is covered in 8 seconds, what distance would be covered in 2 minutes 40 seconds, travelling at the same speed?

8 seconds $\quad$ = 50 metres

1 second $\quad$ = $\frac{50}{8}$ metres (50 ÷ 8)

160 seconds (2 mins. 40 secs) = $\dfrac{50}{1\cancel{8}} \times \dfrac{^{20}\cancel{160}}{1}$ = 1,000 metres.

(3) Peter ran for 40 minutes at an average speed of 18 km/h. How long would it take him to walk the same distance at an average speed of 4 km/h?

To solve this problem, two of the **rules** must be used. The question is asking for the **time** of the journey. To find the time it is necessary to know the **distance**.

The distance is not given, but it can be worked out from the first sentence of the question:-

Distance = Speed × Time $\qquad$ Peter's speed (when running) was 18 km/h

His time (when running) was 40 minutes (or $\frac{2}{3}$ hr).

$18 \times \frac{2}{3}$ = 12 km.

So the distance to be covered in the journey is 12 km.

It is now possible to find the time Peter takes to cover this distance the second time (walking).

Time = Distance ÷ Speed

$\qquad$ = 12 ÷ 4 = 3 hours.

The final example has not been worked out. Work through it carefully to find the answers to each of the three parts.

(4) A train travels from London to Crewe in 2 hours, at an average speed of 125 km/h. The same train then goes on to Preston, which is 336 km from London, at an average speed for the entire journey of 112 km/h.

(a) What is the distance by rail from London to Crewe?
(b) How long would it take to get from London to Preston on this train?
(c) What is the average speed of the train between Crewe and Preston?

CHAPTER NINE

PERIMETER

The perimeter is the distance round a shape, that is, round its edges. The perimeter is found by adding all the edges together.

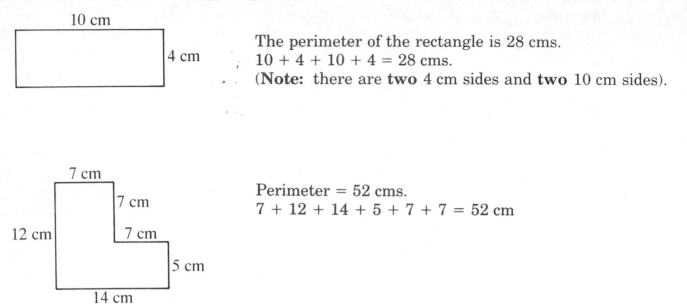

The perimeter of the rectangle is 28 cms.
10 + 4 + 10 + 4 = 28 cms.
(**Note:** there are **two** 4 cm sides and **two** 10 cm sides).

Perimeter = 52 cms.
7 + 12 + 14 + 5 + 7 + 7 = 52 cm

The perimeter is always measured in centimetres, metres, etc.

A box is a solid with 12 edges. On occasion it is necessary to find the total length of the edges of a box.

Example:

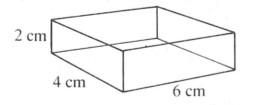

2 cms (height) × 4 = 8 cms
4 cms (width) × 4 = 16 cms
6 cms (length) × 4 = 24 cms

Therefore total length of edges = 48 cms.

TYPICAL QUESTIONS

1. Find the perimeter of:

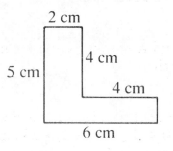

2. Find the perimeter of:

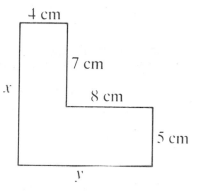

Note: The lengths of two edges are missing: that is x and y. What two lengths add up to x? What two lengths add up to y?

3. Find the length of the edges of the following box:

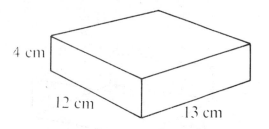

Remember all boxes have 12 edges.

CHAPTER ELEVEN
AREA

The area of a shape is the amount of surface enclosed by its boundaries.

The shaded part is the area of this rectangle.

The area of any shape is measured in squares, usually square metres or square centimetres. So if a room has an area of 20 square metres, it means that 20 squares of side 1 metre will fit into the room.

This represents one square metre, that is, a square of side one metre.

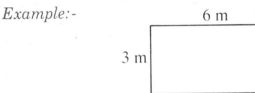

This room has a floor area of 20 square metres, because 20 squares of side one metre will fit into the room. The area can be written as 20 m^2 (or sometimes 20 sq.m.).

To find the area of a square or rectangle, multiply its length by its breadth, remembering the units will be **square** units.

Example:-

Area = 6 m × 3 m = 18 m^2

It may be necessary to divide a shape into two rectangles in order to find its area.

Example:-

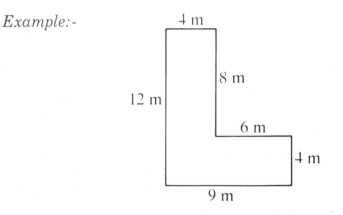

This becomes two separate shapes:-

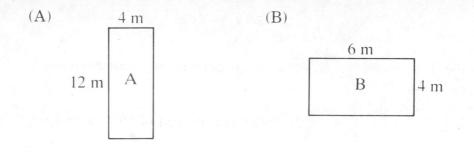

(A) 4 m

12 m | A

(B)

6 m

B   4 m

The area of (A) is 4 m × 12 m = 48 m²   The area of (B) is 6 m × 4 m = 24 m²

Total area = A + B

$$= 48 \text{ m}^2 + 24 \text{ m}^2$$

$$= 72 \text{ m}^2$$

In some questions it is necessary to find the area of a margin.

Example:

A picture is mounted on a backing board. The picture measures 10 cm by 7 cm. If there is a 1 cm margin between the picture and the edge of the frame, what is the area of the frame not covered by the picture?

It is always useful to draw a diagram.

If the length of the picture is 10 cm., then the length of the backing board must be 12 cm., because of the 1 cm margin on **both** sides of the picture.
Similarly the width of the backing board must be 9 cm.

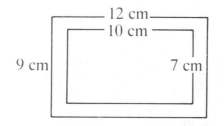

12 cm

10 cm

9 cm

7 cm

The total area of the backing board, including the picture   = 12 × 9 = 108 cm²
The area of the picture   = 10 × 7 = 70 cm²
Therefore the area of the frame not covered by the picture   = 108 − 70 = 38 cm²

SURFACE AREA

CUBOIDS

In maths, the name given to a box is a cuboid.

All cuboids have: (a) six sides (a top, a bottom, front, back and two ends)
                  (b) twelve edges.

There is a special type of cuboid called a cube in which all six sides have the same area and all twelve edges are the same length.

The six sides of a cuboid can be taken apart to make a plan or **net**:-

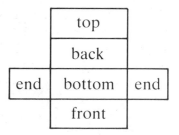

Example: Find the total surface area of a cuboid 5 m × 4 m × 3 m

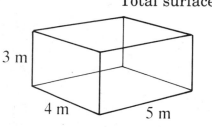

Total surface area = area of all six sides added together

$3 \text{ m} \times 4 \text{ m} = 12 \text{ m}^2 \times 2 = 24 \text{ m}^2$ (two ends)

$4 \text{ m} \times 5 \text{ m} = 20 \text{ m}^2 \times 2 = 40 \text{ m}^2$ (top and bottom)

$3 \text{ m} \times 5 \text{ m} = 15 \text{ m}^2 \times 2 = 30 \text{ m}^2$ (front and back)

Total surface area = 94 m^2

Whilst a box has been defined as a cuboid, there are also many other cuboids, for example, containers, rooms, swimming pools.

UNITS

In one square metre (m^2) there are 10,000 square centimetres (cm^2).

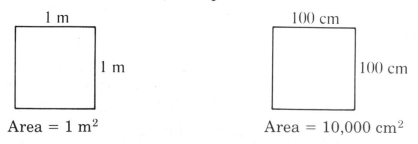

Both squares represent the same area. So $1 \text{ m}^2 = 10,000 \text{ cm}^2$

1 square centimetre (cm^2) = 100 square millimetres (mm^2).

TYPICAL QUESTIONS

1. Find the area of the following:

(i)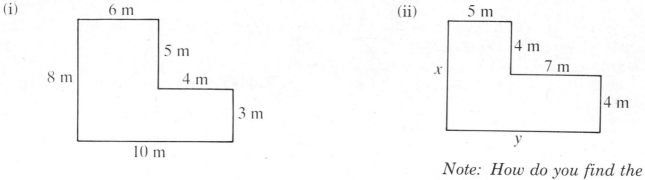

(ii)

Note: How do you find the
lengths of x and y?

2. Find the total surface area of the following cuboid measuring 3 m by 5 m by 10 m.

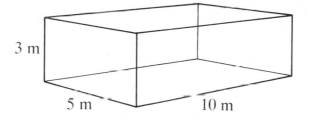

Note: It is necessary to find the area of all six sides and add them together.

CHAPTER TWELVE

VOLUME

The volume of a solid object is the amount of space it takes up, or, if it is a hollow object, the amount of space inside it.

In maths, it is often necessary to work out the volume of cuboids and cubes.

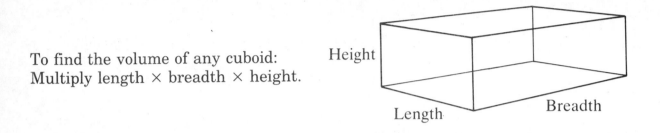

To find the volume of any cuboid:
Multiply length × breadth × height.

The volume is always measured in cubic units.

The following cuboid has a volume of 150 cubic metres:-

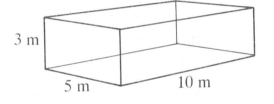

L × B × H = volume

10 m × 5 m × 3 m = 150 cubic metres. This is usually written: 150 m³

This means that 150 cubes of edge 1 metre (as in the diagram below) will fit exactly into the cuboid.

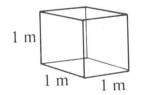

A cube of 1 metre.
Volume = 1 m × 1 m × 1 m = 1 m³
1 cubic metre

Therefore:- 150 × 1 m³ = 150 m³

In one cubic metre there are 1,000,000 cubic cms. This is a difficult number to imagine.

Study the following two diagrams of cubes. Both have the same volume, but it is expressed in different units of measurement.

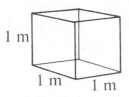

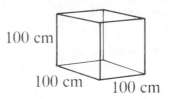

Volume = 1 m × 1 m × 1 m
      = 1 m³

Volume = 100 cm × 100 cm × 100 cm
      = 1,000,000 cm³

Therefore 1 m³ = 1,000,000 cm³

In a cubic metre there are 1000 litres

This means a tank which has a volume of 1 m³ will contain exactly 1000 litres of liquid.

Problems based on volume

Example:-
A container measures 6 m in length, 5 m in width and is 8 m high (6 m by 5 m by 8 m). How many boxes measuring 1 m by 2 m by 3 m will fit into the container?

Space inside the container (volume) = 6 × 5 × 8 = 240 m³

Space taken up by each box (volume) = 1 × 2 × 3 = 6 m³

The number of boxes fitting in the container = 240 ÷ 6 = 40

Example:
A swimming pool is 30 m long and 10 m wide. The pool is filled to a depth of $2\frac{1}{2}$ m with water. How many litres of water are in the pool?

The volume of the pool that is to be filled with water = 30 × 10 × $2\frac{1}{2}$

Multiply using the rules of fractions:

$$\frac{\overset{15}{\cancel{30}}}{1} \times \frac{10}{1} \times \frac{5}{\underset{1}{\cancel{2}}} = 750 \text{ m}^3$$

1000 litres = 1 m³

Therefore 750 × 1000 = 750,000 litres in the pool.

TYPICAL QUESTIONS

1. What is the volume of a cube of edge $\frac{1}{2}$ m?
   Note: In cubes all edges are of the same length.

2. A cuboid's measurements are 4 metres, 2 metres 50 cm and 1 metre 40 cm. What is the volume of the cuboid?

3. A swimming pool 12 m long and 5 m wide is filled to a depth of 2 m. What is the volume of water in the pool?

4. A store room measures 5 m in length and 4 m in width.
   It is filled to a height of 2 m by boxes.
   If each box measures 2 m by 1 m by $\frac{1}{2}$ m., how many boxes will be in the room?

5. A container 12 m long is $2\frac{1}{2}$ m wide. If the volume of the container is 120 m^3 what is the height of the container?

CHAPTER THIRTEEN
AVERAGES

The average amount is obtained by finding the **total amount** and **dividing** the total amount by the **number of items** involved.

Example:-

Three boys, Tom, Harry and Arnold, collected apples from a local orchard. Tom collected 27, Harry 42 and Arnold 63. The total amount collected was 132. The average number of apples collected was 44.

This average was obtained in two stages:

(i) By adding up the amounts (27 + 42 + 63) to give a total amount = 132

(ii) By dividing the total amount by the number of boys = $\dfrac{132}{3}$ = 44

Similarly
John bought seven books priced at £8 each and three books priced at £11 each. Therefore, the average price of the books was £8.90.

(i) 7 × £8 = £56, 3 × £11 = £33
   £33 + £56 = £89. That is the total cost of the books.

(ii) £89 ÷ 10 (Total number of books) = £8.90. This is the average cost of each book.

The average might even appear to be totally improbable.

For example:

In Tom's family there are three children, and in Alison's family there are two children. The average number of children in each family is 2.5.

(i) 3 + 2 = 5. This is the total number of children

(ii) 5 ÷ 2 = 2.5. This is the average number of children in each family.

The following example involves *two* total amounts:

A group of five children had an average age of 13 years. When one of the children left, the group's average age was reduced to $12\frac{1}{2}$ years. How old was the child who left the group?

5 children, average age of 13 had a **total** age of 65 years (5 × 13).
4 children, average age of $12\frac{1}{2}$ had a **total** age of 50 years (4 × $12\frac{1}{2}$).

The difference in total amounts is the age of the child who has left the group. 65 − 50 = 15 years old.

In maths, the word "mean" is used on occasion instead of "average".

TYPICAL QUESTIONS

1. Kate's homework marks during the week are 7, 8, 6, 9 and 4. What was the average mark she received for her homework?

   (*What is unusual about the answer?*)

2. Tom bought three presents at £6.50 each and two other presents at £12.00 each. What was the average price of each present?

   (*Hint: What was the total cost? How many presents were bought?*)

3. Billy's average homework mark after five homeworks was 8. If his first four marks were 6, 10, 7 and 8, what mark did he receive for his fifth homework?

4. A postman started off with 11 parcels. The average weight of the parcels was 3 kg. After he had delivered the first parcel, the average weight of the remaining parcels fell to $2\frac{1}{2}$ kg. What was the weight of the parcel he had delivered?

   (*Hint: What was the total weight of the 11 parcels? What was the total weight of the 10 parcels?*)

5. Four boys had an average mark of 67%. Six girls had an average mark of 71%. What was the average mark of the whole group of boys and girls?

CHAPTER FOURTEEN

UNEQUAL SHARING

This is when a quantity is **not** divided into equal parts or shares.

Such problems are often recognised by the words "more than", "greater than", "fewer than", "difference", etc.

Example: A piece of rope, 190 cm long, is cut into two pieces so that one piece is 44 cm longer than the other. What is the length of each piece?

This is carried out in three stages:

(i) Subtract the difference between the amounts from the total amount.

So, in the example, subtract the difference between the lengths of the two pieces from the total length.

190 cm − 44 cm = 146 cm.

(ii) Divide the answer by 2. This will give the smaller amount.
In the example, this will be the shorter length.

$$\begin{array}{r} 73 \\ 2\overline{)146} \end{array}$$ 73 cm = the shorter piece.

(iii) To find the larger amount, add the difference in amounts to the smaller amount.

In the example, add the difference, 44 cm, to the 73 cm:

44 + 73 = 117 cm = longer piece.

Check your answer by:-

a) **Adding the two parts together, making sure they add up to the total amount.**
   In this case 73 + 117 = 190 cm.

b) **Making sure the difference in amounts equals the difference stated in the question.**
   That is, 117 − 73 = 44 cm. The answer is therefore correct.

A More Difficult Example

Peter, Paul and Joanne have 300 marbles. Peter and Paul have 60 marbles more than Joanne. Peter has 24 more marbles than Paul. How many marbles does each child have?

This type of problem involves an extra process.
Firstly, treat Peter and Paul as only one person.

Then work out how many marbles Joanne has.

(i) Subtract the difference in amounts between Peter/Paul and Joanne from the whole amount: 300 − 60 = 240

(ii) Divide the answer by 2.

$$\frac{120}{2)240}$$ So Joanne's share is: 120.

(iii) Add the difference in amounts to Joanne's share to find Peter/Paul's share:

120 + 60 = 180

This 180 now has to be divided between Peter and Paul. Repeat the same stages. Peter must have 24 more than Paul.

(i) 180 − 24 = 156

(ii) $$\frac{78}{2)156}$$ So Paul's share is 78.

(iii) 78 + 24 = 102. So Peter's share is 102.

Check your answer by adding the shares:-

a) 102 + 78 + 120 = 300

b) Peter/Paul 180 − Joanne 120 = 60

c) Peter 102 − Paul 78 = 24.

TYPICAL QUESTIONS

1. Michael and Stephen have a total of £6.40. Michael has £1.80 more than Stephen. How much do they each have?

2. The sum of two numbers is 180. The difference between the numbers is 54. What are the two numbers?
(*This time the question involves numbers, not people. Call the unknown numbers x and y in your calculation.*)

3. In one year Liverpool and Manchester United scored a total of 180 goals. Liverpool scored 30 goals fewer than Manchester United. How many goals did United score?

4. Three boys collected £220 for charity. Tom and James together collected £120 more than Arthur. Tom collected £30 more than James. How much did they each collect?
(*Start by treating Tom and James as one person, then separate them again after working out Arthur's amount.*)

CHAPTER FIFTEEN
RATIO SHARING

Ratio sharing is when a quantity is first divided into equal parts and then these equal parts are distributed in an unequal way.

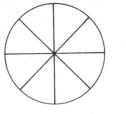

This cake has been divided into 8 equal pieces

If John has three pieces and Peter has five pieces, then the cake can be said to have been divided in the **ratio** of 3 to 5.
This can be written as 3 : 5.
Frequently, ratio sharing can be recognised by the word "times".

Example: Ben and Tom collected £400. Ben collected seven times as much as Tom. How much did they each collect?

This is carried out in five stages:-

(i) **Let the smaller share = 1 part.** (Tom)

(ii) **Work out the larger share.**
In this case the larger share is seven times greater. $1 \times 7 = 7$ parts. (Ben)

(iii) **Add up the number of parts.** $1 + 7 = 8$ parts.

(iv) **To find the value of one part, divide the total amount by the number of parts.** £400 ÷ 8 = £50.

(v) **Multiply each part by the value of one part.**
Therefore, the smaller share (1 part) = $1 \times £50 = £50$.
        The larger share (7 parts) = $7 \times £50 = £350$.

Examples of more complicated ratio sharing questions:

1. At a pop concert, 3 girls entered for every 2 boys. At the concert there were 2400 children. How many girls were there?

    The ratio = 3 girls : 2 boys.
    This means that in every 5 children there were 3 girls.
    That is, $\frac{3}{5}$ of the children were girls.

    Apply the rules of fractions:-

    $\frac{3}{5}$ of 2400 = $\frac{3}{5} \times \frac{2400}{1}$ = 1440 girls attending the concert.

2. Ice creams were priced at 20p and 25p. For every expensive one, two cheaper ones were purchased. If £13 was spent, how many ice creams were bought?

2 of the 20p ice creams for every 1 of the 25p ice creams.
For every 65 pence (20p + 20p + 25p), three ice creams were bought.

In £13 there are 20 lots of 65p:

$$\begin{array}{r} 20 \\ 65\overline{)1300} \\ 130 \\ \hline 00 \end{array}$$

Since for every 65p, 3 ice creams are bought, then a total of 60 ice creams are purchased (20 × 3 = 60).

3. John scored twice as many goals as Fred. Fred scored three times more than Alec. If they scored 40 altogether, how many goals did they each score?

Smallest share   = 1 (Alec)
Second share   = 3 (Fred) 3 times more than Alec (3 × 1)
Third share   = 6 (John) 2 times more than Fred (2 × 3)

Therefore, the total number of parts = 10   (1 + 3 + 6)
Each part = 4 (40 goals divided by ten parts)
Therefore, Alec = 4 (1 × 4), Fred = 12 (3 × 4), John = 24 (6 × 4)
Alec scored four goals, Fred twelve goals, and John twenty-four goals.

Check: 4 + 12 + 24 = 40 goals scored.

TYPICAL QUESTIONS

1. Fiona and her brother Iain obtained a total of 120 house points during a school term. Fiona obtained three times as many as Iain. How many house points did they each obtain?

2. In a survey conducted in a junior school it was found that on one evening four times as many children watched BBC 1 as watched BBC 2, and that twice as many children watched ITV as watched BBC 1. If there were 310 children in the school, how many children watched each channel?

CHAPTER SIXTEEN
UNITARY METHOD

Look at these problems:-

Example 1: Seven apples cost 42p. How much would four apples cost?

Example 2: Nine men take 36 days to build a wall. How long would four men take?

The golden rule in all these problems is to find the cost, value, length of time, etc., of **one**.

Common sense must be used to decide whether to divide or multiply to obtain **one**.

In Example 1: 7 apples cost 42p.
    1 apple costs 42p ÷ 7 = 6p
(Common sense: if multiplied one apple would cost £2.94)
Therefore: 4 apples cost 6p × 4 = 24p

In Example 2: 9 men take 36 days.
    1 man takes 36 × 9 = 324 days
(Common sense: 1 man must take longer than 9 men, so it must be a multiplication sum.)
Therefore: 4 men take 324 ÷ 4 = 81 days

Occasionally if division is difficult, a problem needs to be looked at very closely:-

Example 3: If 3 apples cost 19p, find the cost of 21 apples.

To find the cost of 1 apple (by dividing 19p by 3) will give a difficult amount with which to work.

Look for another way:-

In this case, there is a relationship between 3 apples and 21 apples. Twenty one is *seven times* greater than three. Accordingly twenty one apples will cost seven times as much as three apples. So, find the cost of seven times as many apples.

Therefore, the cost will be:- 19p × 7 = £1.33
    21 apples will cost £1.33

TYPICAL QUESTIONS

1. If 5 books cost £7.75, find the cost of 11 books.

2. If 11 pens cost £4.50, find the cost of 44 pens.

CHAPTER SEVENTEEN

FACTORS

One number is a factor of another number when it can be divided exactly into that number.

For instance, 3 is a factor of 12 because it divides exactly into 12. In the same way, 2, 4 and 6 are factors of 12, but 5 is not because when 5 is divided into 12 there is a remainder of 2.
In the same way 2, 4, 5, 8, 10 and 20 are all factors of 40.

Prime Factors

A prime number is a number which can only be divided by itself and 1. It has no other factors. So 13 is a prime number: nothing will divide into it exactly, except itself (13) and 1.

A prime factor is a number which is both a factor and a prime number.

So, whilst 4, 8, 10 and 20 are factors of 40, only 2 and 5 are prime factors of 40.

To find the prime factors of any number, divide that number by the **lowest** prime number that will divide into it exactly. Keep on dividing by the lowest prime number until the answer is 1.

Example:-
To find the prime factors of 30:

2 | 30	the lowest prime number which will divide into 30 is 2, giving an answer of 15.
3 | 15	the lowest prime number which will divide into 15 is 3, giving an answer of 5.
5 | 5	the lowest prime number which will divide into 5 is 5, giving an answer of 1.
1	

There must never be a remainder.
The divisors are the prime factors, so the prime factors of 30 are 2, 3 and 5.

Prime factors are used in solving problems.

Example:-

A headmaster has the choice of dividing his pupils into groups of 20, 30 or 45 for the school's Christmas party. What is the lowest number of pupils there could be in the school?

Three stages are followed
(i) Find the prime factors of 20, 30 and 45:

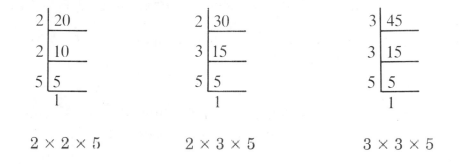

$$2 \times 2 \times 5 \qquad 2 \times 3 \times 5 \qquad 3 \times 3 \times 5$$

(ii) Draw a bracket. In this bracket put the factors of each number. Make sure no factor is missed out. If a factor or factors are already in the bracket it is wrong to write them in again since the **lowest** number of pupils is required.

$(2 \times 2 \times 3 \times 3 \times 5)$

Note: The factors of 20 $(2 \times 2 \times 5)$ are all included
The factors of 30 $(2 \times 3 \times 5)$ are all included
The factors of 45 $(3 \times 3 \times 5)$ are all included

(iii) Multiply the numbers in the bracket.

$2 \times 2 \times 3 \times 3 \times 5 = 180$

Therefore, 180 pupils is the lowest number of pupils in the school.

In this example 180 is the lowest number 20, 30 and 45 will each divide into exactly.

This number is said to be the **Lowest Common Multiple** of 20, 30 and 45. It is usually referred to as the **"L.C.M."**

The **Highest Common Factor** or **"H.C.F."** is the highest number that will divide into a group of numbers.

Example: Find the H.C.F. of 30, 45 and 90.

Three stages are followed
(i) Find the prime factors of the three numbers:

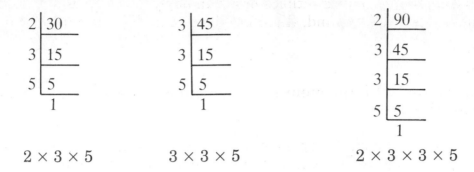

$$2 \times 3 \times 5 \qquad 3 \times 3 \times 5 \qquad 2 \times 3 \times 3 \times 5$$

(ii) Find the factor or group of factors, which are **common** to each of these three numbers. This means they appear among the factors of all the numbers.

3 and 5 are the factors found in all three numbers.

(iii) Multiply the "common" factors to find the **Highest Common Factor:** $3 \times 5 = 15$

So 15 is the **H.C.F.** of 30, 45 and 90.

TYPICAL QUESTIONS

1. How many prime factors divide into 210?

2. Find the prime factors of (a) 16 and (b) 42.

3. What is the highest number that will divide into 42, 105 and 210?

4. There are sufficient sheep on a farm to divide into groups of 30, 35 and 42 for shearing. What is the lowest number of sheep that could be on the farm?
   Hint: Study the example of the lowest number of pupils in the school.

5. The three bells on a church tower chime every 6, 30 and 35 minutes. How many times do they chime together in a period of 21 hours, given that they all chime together at midnight?

   Hint: First, find the L.C.M. of 6, 30 and 35.
   This will indicate the time interval before the bells strike together again.
   Secondly, divide the L.C.M. into 21 hours. This will give the number of times the bells strike together in that time.

CHAPTER EIGHTEEN
SETS

The word **set** in maths is the name given to a number of items which have something in common. For example, 5, 10, 15, 20, 25 make up a set of numbers. The common "something" is that they are all multiples of 5. Similarly $\frac{8}{7}$, $\frac{9}{4}$, $\frac{15}{11}$ and $\frac{13}{4}$ make up a set. They are all improper fractions and, therefore, belong to a set of improper fractions.

The Elements

The items in a set are called the **members** or **elements** of a set. Usually a circle is put round the members of a set.

The circle represents a set. Set A is a set of numbers between 1 and 26 which are all multiples of 5.

The symbol ∈ represents membership of a set.

Example: 10 ∈ A. That means 10 is a member of set A.

An alternative way of illustrating the members of a set is by brackets.

Set A = {5, 10, 20, 25}

The Intersection

It is possible for the members of a set to belong to more than one set.
For example, Set P = {1, 2, 3, 5, 7}. It is a set of all the prime numbers below 10.
Set T = {2, 4, 6, 8}. It is a set of all the even numbers below 10.

"2" is a member of both Set P and Set T.

The membership of two sets can be shown in two ways

(1) The sign ∩ represents the intersection of two sets. (The ∩ is sometimes called **cap**) That is, the members which belong to both sets. In the example:-

P ∩ T = 2 (P "cap" T is 2)

(2)

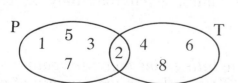

In this diagram the circles representing the sets overlap and 2 is the intersection.

Universal Set

When more than one circle is shown it is usual to put both circles in a rectangle. This rectangle represents what is called the **universal set**: that is, it contains the members of both sets.

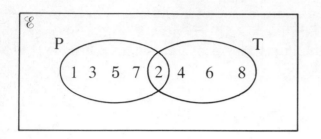

The rectangle $\mathscr{E}$ represents the universal set.

The above diagram is named a **Venn** diagram.

Note: Sets do not simply apply to numbers. There can be sets of people, colours, books: in fact anything at all.

Sub-sets

A **sub-set** is the name given to a set which is part of a larger set.

Example:-
Set N is a set of boys' names.
Set A is a set of boys' names beginning with the letter "A".
Since **all** the members of set A are also members of set N it is said that A is a sub-set of N.

The symbol ⊂ represents this idea.

In this case it can be written: A ⊂ N. This can be shown in a diagram:-

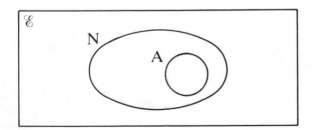

Problem Solving by Sets

Sets are useful in solving certain mathematical problems.

Example:-
In a group of 20 children, 17 have a cat and 13 have a dog. How many (i) have both a cat and dog? (ii) have **only** a dog?

Let Set D = those who have a dog. Set D has 13 members.
Let Set C = those who have a cat. Set C has 17 members.
Add together Sets D and C. This gives a total of 30 members.
Since there are only 20 children altogether, this means that 10 members must belong to both sets $(30 - 20 = 10)$. This can be shown in a Venn diagram:-

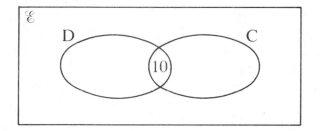

Once we have the value of D ∩ C the remainder of the diagram can be completed.

There are 13 members in set D. Since 10 have already been put into the circle representing set D, then 3 must be added to the circle, but **not** in that part of the circle which overlaps with C.
Similarly, in set C there are 17 members. 10 have been already included in the circle representing C, therefore 7 have to be added to the circle but in that part that does **not** overlap with (d)

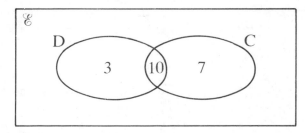

13 have a dog **but** 3 have **only** a dog.
17 have a cat **but** 7 have **only** a cat.
10 have **both** a cat and a dog.

$3 + 10 + 7 = 20$. Therefore 20 equals the entire group or universal set ($\mathscr{E}$).

The Union

When the members of two sets are added the symbol ∪ is used. The symbol represents the **union** of two sets. (The ∪ is sometimes called: **cup**.)

So in the example: D ∪ C = 20 (D "cup" C equals 20)

65

Note the following question and the Venn diagram used to answer the question.

In a group of 20, 17 have a cat, 13 have a dog and 2 have neither a cat nor dog. How many have both?

If the set of cat owners and the set of dog owners are added, plus the two members of the group who have neither then the result is 32: (17 + 13 + 2). Since there are only 20 in the group, 12 must have both a cat and a dog.

There are 17 in the set of cat owners. Since 12 also have a dog, then there are 5 who have a cat only.

There are 13 in the set of dog owners. Since 12 also have a cat, then there is 1 who has only a dog.

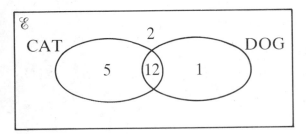

Note the "2". These two people form part of the group but are not in either of the sets.

When all the members of the two sets and those who are not members of either set are added together, the result equals the total number in the group. The result of this addition is the universal set: $\mathscr{E} = 20$.

TYPICAL QUESTIONS

1. Set A is a set of prime numbers between 40 and 60. How many members in Set A?

2. In a group of 50 people, 29 enjoy tea and 35 enjoy coffee. How many enjoy both tea and coffee?

3. In a group of 100 schoolchildren, 56 have a dog, 41 have a cat, whilst 23 have no animals. How many only have a dog?
   Hint: How many have both?

4. In a group, $\frac{1}{2}$ enjoy coffee and $\frac{5}{8}$ enjoy tea. If 5 enjoy both, how many are in the group?
   Hint: What fraction enjoy both?

5.

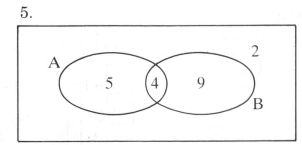

How many elements in:

(i) A ∩ B
(ii) A ∪ B
(iii) The universal set?

CHAPTER NINETEEN

THE BINARY SYSTEM

In earlier sections it was stated that our number system is based on groups of ten. The place value of digits increased/decreased by ten as the digit was moved to the left or right. This number system is called "Denary".

In Binary, the number system is based on groups of **two**. The place value of digits increases/decreases by two as the digit is moved to the left or right.

Instead of thousands, hundreds, tens and units, there are different column values.

Sixteens	*Eights*	*Fours*	*Twos*	*Units*
eight twos (8 × 2)	four twos (4 × 2)	two twos (2 × 2)	one two (1 × 2)	one

To convert binary numbers into denary numbers

1011 in base two will have a denary equivalent of 11. This can be explained by studying the column headings:

8   4   2   u

$$1 \quad 0 \quad 1 \quad 1 = (1 \times 8) + (0 \times 4) + (1 \times 2) + (1 \times 1)$$
$$= 8 + 0 + 2 + 1 = 11$$

Similarly 11011 in base two will have a denary equivalent of 27:

16   8   4   2   u

$$1 \quad 1 \quad 0 \quad 1 \quad 1 = (1 \times 16) + (1 \times 8) + (0 \times 4) + (1 \times 2) + (1 \times 1)$$
$$= 16 + 8 + 0 + 2 + 1 = 27$$

To convert denary numbers to binary numbers

Example: Convert 11 into a binary, or base two number:

Two stages need to be followed:

(i) Divide the denary number by 2. Write in the remainder (R) even when the remainder is 0. Keep dividing until the dividend (that is, the answer) is 0.

```
2 | 11
2 | 5 R 1
2 | 2 R 1
2 | 1 R 0
    0 R 1
```

(ii) Write down the remainders starting from the last remainder.

```
2 | 11
2 | 5 R1
2 | 2 R1        ↑
2 | 1 R0
    0 R1
```

The binary equivalent of 11 is 1011

67

The result can be checked by re-converting the binary number into base 10.

$$\begin{array}{cccc} \mathbf{8} & \mathbf{4} & \mathbf{2} & \mathbf{u} \\ 1 & 0 & 1 & 1 \end{array} = (1 \times 8) + (0 \times 4) + (1 \times 2) + (1 \times 1)$$

$$8 + 0 + 2 + 1 = 11$$

THE FOUR RULES

Addition

When adding in the binary system, remember all working is in groups of 2.

Example: 1 + 1 + 1

This is set out:

1		1
1		1
1 +		1 +
		11

1 + 1 + 1 = 3
3 contains **one** group of 2 to be carried and one left over

```
   1
   1
   1 +
  11
   1
```

Example: 1 + 1 + 1 + 1 + 1

This is set out:

```
    1                                          1
    1                                          1
    1                                          1
    1                                          1
    1 +                                        1 +
                                             101
                                            1 2
```

1 + 1 + 1 + 1 + 1 = 5
That is **two** groups of 2 to be carried and one left over.
The 2 carried becomes one group of 2 to be carried and 0 left over.

Study the following addition:

```
   101
 + 111
   110
 10010
 1 2 1 1
```

Starting with the unit column:
1 + 1 = 2. That is, one group of two to be carried leaving no remainder.
1 + 1 + the 1 carried = 3. That is, one group of two to be carried with one remainder.
1 + 1 + 1 + the 1 carried = 4. That is two groups of two to be carried with no remainder.

Finally, the 2 carried forms a new column. This becomes one group of two to be carried with no remainder.

68

Subtraction

When subtracting, if there is a need to borrow, as the sum is base two, borrow two.

For example: 110 − 1

```
1 9̸²0
    1 −
1 0 1
```

A useful check is to add the bottom line of the sum to the answer: this will give the top line:

```
  1
101 +
110
 1
```

Multiplication

In muliplication, the same rules of multiplication apply as in base ten, **except** that in the adding process remember the addition is in base two.

For example: 101 × 11

```
 101
  11 ×
 101
1010
1111
```

Division

In division, the same rules of division apply as in base ten **except** that in subtracting for the remainder the subtraction is in base two:

Example: 1111 ÷ 101

```
      11
101)1111
    101
    101
    101
```

It is useful to check the answer. This is done by multiplying the answer of the sum by the original divisor, ensuring that the result is the dividend of the original sum:

```
 101
  11 ×
 101
1010
1111
```

TYPICAL QUESTIONS

1) Convert into base two numbers: (i) 17, (ii) 39.

2) Convert into base ten numbers: (i) 10101, (ii) 110111.

3) Work out the following sums in base two. All the numbers are in base two:

(i)   101
       11
    111 +

(ii) 10100
     111 −
     ‾‾‾‾‾‾‾

(iii)   10101
      101 ×

(iv) 111)$\overline{1011011}$

4) Carry out the following operations when the numbers given are all in the binary system:-

a)   101 + 11
b)   1011 + 111 + 101 + 1101
c)   1101 − 1011
d)   1000 − 11
e)   101 × 11
f)   1101 × 101
g)   10101 ÷ 11
h)   110111 ÷ 101
i)   (1101 + 111) − 1111
(*Note: Work out the bracket first.*)

CHAPTER TWENTY

GRAPHS

In maths, information is usually given in the form of figures or words. Information, however, can also be expressed in graphs and charts.

Example:-

During one week in February, the number of absences in the Infant Department of a school was recorded. The information (**data**) collected could be represented in the following graphs.

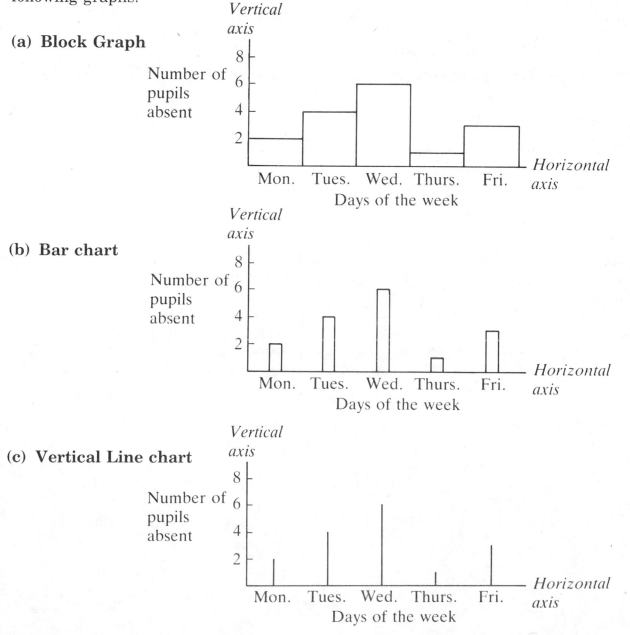

(a) Block Graph

(b) Bar chart

(c) Vertical Line chart

In reading any of these types of graph, three steps need to be taken:-

(1) Study each axis carefully. The vertical axis is the line going up at the side of the graph. The horizontal axis is the line going along the bottom of the graph.

So in the three examples of graphs on the previous page, the vertical axes refer to the number of pupils absent. The horizontal axes refer to the days of the week.

(2) Always look very closely at the numbers on the axes of graphs. They are not always one, two, three, four.

The gaps between the numbers are called the intervals.

Notice that in the examples given, the intervals on the vertical axes refer to two pupils, not to one.

(3) Take time to read the information properly, and to understand it.

In the example used here, two children were absent on Monday, four on Tuesday, six on Wednesday, one on Thursday, and three on Friday.

(d) Pie Charts

Example:-

A group of 24 children were asked to state their favourite colour. The information they provided was then shown in the form of a pie chart:-

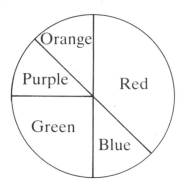

The circle represents the 'whole': that is, the twenty four children. The segments into which it has been divided represent the numbers preferring each different colour.

To discover from this chart how many children preferred each of the colours, it is necessary to divide the circle up completely into **equal** segments, each of them the same size as the **smallest** segment in the pie chart. (In fact the Orange, Purple and Blue segments are all equally small.)

This is the result:-

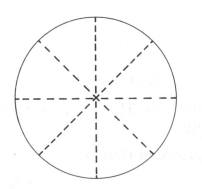

From this it is clear that there are eight equal segments. So the circle has been divided into eighths.

72

Now the original pie chart and the equally divided circle can be put together:-

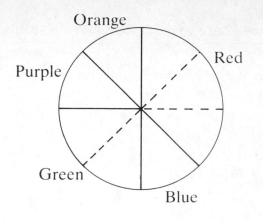

It is now possible to work out the number of children represented by each segment:-

Total number of children= 24 (whole circle)

RED $\qquad$ = 3 segments $\qquad$ $= \dfrac{3}{8}$

$\qquad$ $\dfrac{3}{8}$ of 24 $\qquad$ $= \dfrac{3}{8} \times \dfrac{24}{1} = 9$ children

GREEN $\qquad$ = 2 segments $\qquad$ $= \dfrac{2}{8}$ or $\dfrac{1}{4}$

$\qquad$ $\dfrac{1}{4}$ of 24 $\qquad$ $= \dfrac{1}{4} \times \dfrac{24}{1} = 6$ children

BLUE $\qquad$ = 1 segment $\qquad$ $= \dfrac{1}{8}$

$\qquad$ $\dfrac{1}{8}$ of 24 $\qquad$ $= \dfrac{1}{8} \times \dfrac{24}{1} = 3$ children

PURPLE and ORANGE are the same as BLUE – 3 children each.

With all pie charts, the rule is always to find out what fraction each division of the chart represents.

DEGREES

Sometimes the size of the segments on a pie chart is shown in **degrees**.

Any circle can be divided into 360 equal parts, known as degrees. The word 'degrees' is shown by a small circle after the number: 360° 90° 45° etc.

In the above example, the information might have been provided that 45° of the circle represented those who liked the colour blue.

Since there are 360° in a circle, 45° can be shown as a fraction of 360: $\dfrac{45}{360}$

It can then be cancelled down to discover what fraction preferred blue, and this can be converted into the actual number in the same way as above:-

$$\dfrac{45}{360} = \dfrac{9}{72} = \dfrac{1}{8} \qquad \dfrac{1}{8} \text{ of } 24 = 3$$

(e) Line Graph

This is a time:distance graph. It represents the distance covered in a journey over a period of time.

To read this type of graph, the following stages need to be followed:

(i) As with bar charts, study the vertical and horizontal axes. Ask what each represents.

(ii) Study the intervals on both axes.

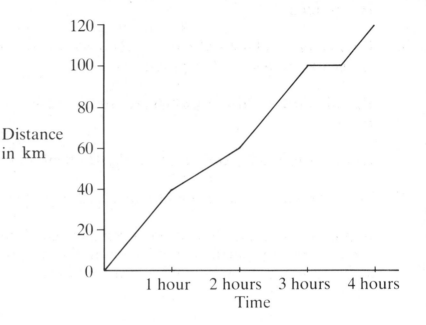

(iii)   Read the graph with care and accuracy.

In the example:

In the first hour 40 km are covered, but in the second hour only 20 km are covered. (60 − 40 = 20).

Also, at a distance of 100 km., there is a rest period of half an hour (no extra distance covered).

In addition to reading the graph, specific questions might be asked:-

What is the total distance covered?   *Answer* = 120 km

What is the total time taken for the journey?   *Answer* = 4 hours

What is the average speed?   *Answer* = $\dfrac{120}{4}$ = 30 km/hr.

74

CHAPTER TWENTY-ONE

PROBLEM SOLVING

The following approach is perhaps the most useful:

(a) Read the problem slowly, carefully reading every word. Then read the problem again.

(b) If there is a worked example, try and work through the example before tackling the problem.

(c) Completely understand what is required in the problem and decide what operation is necessary to solve the problem.

(d) Put all working down on paper, since evidence of a logical approach often carries marks.

(e) Always work accurately and check all calculations.

(f) When an answer has been obtained, ask whether that answer is a sensible one.

In many examinations, it is becoming usual to include problems which do not conform to any particular rules or methods. These questions are designed to test skills of problem solving and logical thinking.

Example: To find the "Connor" of a number, multiply the number by one more than itself and divide the result by 2. For example, the "Connor" of 6 is 21 because $6 \times 7 = 42$ and $42 \div 2 = 21$.

(a) What is the Connor of 13?
(b) What is the difference between the Connor of 12 and the Connor of 20?

Method:-

(a) Multiply 13 by one more than itself $= 13 \times 14 = 182$

The result is then divided by 2: $= 182 \div 2 = 91$

(b) The Connor of 12 $= (12 \times 13) \div 2 = 78$

The Connor of 20 $= (20 \times 21) \div 2 = 210$

The difference $= 210 - 78 = 132$

Practise problem solving techniques on the following typical examples:

1. Horace Miser always kept one penny and two pence coins that came into his possession. In how many ways could he arrange these coins to total 14 pence?

Method:-

1 penny	2 pence
14	—
12	1 etc.

In how many ways could the same amount be arranged if he added a five pence coin to his supply of one penny and two pence coins?

Method:-

1 penny	2 pence	5 pence
9	—	1
7	1	1 etc.

2. In the following diagram, the letters x and y stand for single digit numbers. The numbers are such that any two numbers add up to a square number, so $x + x$ adds up to a square number and $y + x$ adds up to a square number.

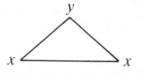

What numbers could x and y stand for?

(Hint: x must be half of an even square number. Square numbers are defined on page six. There are many possible answers to this question).

3. The number 15 can be expressed as the sum of consecutive numbers in two ways:-

$7 + 8 = 15$

$4 + 5 + 6 = 15$

The number 45 can be expressed as the sum of consecutive numbers in five ways. What are these?

(Hint: This is done by trial and error. First, try two consecutive numbers, then three consecutive numbers.)

PRACTICE PAPERS

TEST 1

1. Express sixty one thousand seven hundred and nineteen in figures.

2. How many times can 917 be divided by 17?

3. Christine spent $\frac{3}{8}$ of her money. This left her with £15.00. How much did she start with?

4. Tom obtained 18 marks out of a possible 40 marks in an exercise. Express this as a percentage.

5. What is the value of 0.17 of £4,000?

6. A farmer has 400 metres of fencing. He arranges the fencing in the shape of a square. What is the area of the square?

7. Find the volume of the following shape.

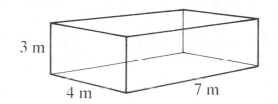

8. Four boys are aged 8 years 6 months, 9 years 3 months, 11 years 10 months and 13 years 1 month. What is the average age of the boys?

9. How many minutes are there between 10.35 a.m. and 1.05 p.m.?

10. A ski lift travels up a mountain at a speed of 5 m per second. What is this speed expressed in km/h?

11. Two numbers add up to 186. The difference between the numbers is 20. What are the two numbers?

12. Divide 200 apples into two piles so that one pile contains four times as many apples as the other.

13. If 6 books cost £33, how much would 17 books cost?

14. What are the prime factors of 182?

15. In a group of 20 children, 17 had a cat and 9 had a dog. How many had both a cat and a dog?

16. Add 101 and 111, when both these numbers are in base two.

TEST 2

1. Express 101,007 in words.

2. What is the lowest number which needs to be added to 871 to make it exactly divisible by 19?

3. If $\frac{3}{4}$ of $\frac{5}{6}$ of a number is 30, what is the number?

4. A box of 400 apples was found to contain 7% which were bad. How many bad apples were in the box?

5. Which is the larger amount and by how much:- 0.3 of £40, or 0.03 of £600?

6. Find the area and perimeter of this shape.

7. How many cubic centimetres are there in a box measuring $\frac{1}{2}$ m by $\frac{1}{3}$ m by 3 m?

8. Four parcels weigh an average of 4 kg each. Two more parcels have an average weight of 5 kg 320 g. What is the average weight of the parcels?

9. A motorist covers a distance of 100 km in 2 hours and then returns at an average speed of 40 km/h. How long does the whole journey take?

10. A plane left Gatwick at 10.45 a.m. and arrived at its destination at 2.15 p.m. How long did the journey last?

11. Jackie and Kathryn weigh a total of 146 kg. Jackie weighs 4 kg more than Kathryn. How much do they each weigh?

12. On a journey to school, Alice travels by bus nine times as many metres as she walks. If the total distance to school is $4\frac{1}{2}$ km., how far does she walk?

13. If 9 pens cost 61 pence, what would be the cost of 72 pens?

14. What is the highest common factor of the following numbers: 30, 105 and 180?

15. A class was asked whether they enjoyed Maths and English. 12 enjoyed Maths, 13 enjoyed English, 10 enjoyed both subjects and two disliked both. How many were in the class?

16. Subtract 11 from 1010, when both these numbers are in base two.

TEST 3

1. Increase ninety six thousand seven hundred and fifty six by two thousand eight hundred and ninety seven.

2. A coach driver is allowed to drive for 6 hours 45 minutes each day. How many hours driving does he do in a period of 9 working days?

3. When $\frac{3}{4}$ is added to a number and the result is divided by $\frac{1}{4}$, the answer is $3\frac{4}{5}$. What was the original number?

4. A painting valued at £40,000 increased in value by 12% over a 5 year period. What was its value after five years?

5. After he had completed 0.85 of his journey, Fred found he still had 9 km to travel. What was the full distance of his journey?

6. A swimming pool measures 8 m by 5 m. It is surrounded by a tiled area 2 m wide. What is the area of the tiled section?

7. A container measuring 10 m by 5 m is filled to a height of 2 m with boxes. The boxes are all cubes, each edge measuring 1 m. How many boxes are in the container?

8. In nine exams a girl had an average mark of 83. If her worst result was not included, the average mark increased to 85. What was her worst mark?

9. School starts at 9.15 a.m. and finishes at 4.00 p.m. Every day there are two breaks, lasting 15 minutes each and a lunch break of one hour. In a five day period, how long are the children in the classroom?

10. Roberta normally left home at 8.35 a.m. and arrived at school at 8.50 a.m., cycling at an average speed of 20 km/h. One day her father took her to school by car. If the journey lasted four minutes, what was her father's average speed?

11. John and Brian together have £20 more than Edward. John has £4 more than Brian. If they have £240 altogether, how much do they each have?

12. James scored three times as many goals as William, but only half the number Harry scored. Altogether they scored 30 goals. How many goals did each boy score?

13. If 5 men repair a roof, the job takes 18 days. How long would it take 3 men to repair the same roof?

14. Whilst Peter climbed the ladder 2 rungs at a time, George 3 rungs at a time and Paul 4 at a time, they were all able to climb the ladder in an exact number of steps. What is the lowest number of rungs the ladder would possess?

15. A group of 30 girls was asked whether they liked pop music or jazz music. 14 enjoyed pop music and 8 enjoyed both. How many enjoyed jazz?

16. $(1101 + 111) \times 101$ — when all the numbers are in base two.

79

TEST 4

1. Reduce one hundred and ninety six thousand four hundred and eighty four by two thousand eight hundred and ninety nine.

2. To make a certain dress, 3.5 m of material is required. How many dresses could be made from a piece of material 90 metres long?

3. Alan spent $\frac{1}{5}$ of his money on sweets and $\frac{1}{4}$ of the remainder on his train fare. This left him with £6. How much did he start with?

4. The value of a car fell by 20% to £8,000. What was the original value of the car?

5. When 0.5 is added to a decimal number and the result is multiplied by 5, the final answer is 4.5. What was the original number?

6. A piece of paper 30 cm long and 16 cm wide has a 2 cm margin cut off all the way round. What area of the paper remains?

7. A pool measuring 25 m by 10 m is filled to a depth of $1\frac{1}{2}$ m. What is the amount of water in the pool expressed in (a) cubic metres (b) litres?

8. The average temperature for the first four days of a seven day holiday was 68°. What was the average daily temperature of the last three days if the average for the entire holiday was 70°?

9. David travelled 180 miles to London at an average speed of 45 km/h and returned at an average speed of 60 km/h. What was the average speed of his journey?

10. When it is twelve noon in Manchester, it is 7.00 a.m. in New York. A plane leaves Manchester at 11.30 a.m. and arrives in New York $5\frac{1}{2}$ hours later. What time is this in New York?

11. Two football teams scored 146 goals last season. One of the teams scored 16 more goals than the other. How many goals did they each score?

12. Jean and Ann collected four times as much paper as Pat. Jean collected 8 kg more than Ann. If they collected 120 kg altogether, how much did they each collect?

13. Rachel decided that if she ate three biscuits a day her supply of biscuits would last her 16 days. How long would the supply last if she ate 8 biscuits a day?

14. Whilst a father's stride is 90 cm., his young son's stride is 60 cm. They start together and walk 1.8 km. How many times will they be in step on the walk?

15. In a group $\frac{3}{4}$ enjoy tea and $\frac{2}{3}$ enjoy coffee. If 35 people enjoy both, how many are in the group?

16. How many different base two numbers can be made using three digits?

80